The Birth
of a Book

Like many things in life, this book began as an idea. The idea concerned a need of many people — the need for better information on marijuana, a subject affecting every person today.

This book places marijuana in the context of reality — The "Big Picture," so to speak. All facts presented are in perspective with unanswered research questions, conflicting information, and the entire social scene.

This unique and colorful book should be of interest to students in junior high and high school, as well as to their parents and other adults. For many adults, it offers a view into a slightly new world, the "drug scene." A world, in reality, not so far removed from the "adult scene" as some people think.

MARIJUANA
Time for a Closer Look

by Curtis L. Janeczek

Illustrated by Ann L. Schreck

Foreword by Robert L. DuPont, M.D.

Healthstar Publications

Columbus, Ohio

Published by:

Questions, comments, and in-
quiries on group rates may be
directed to:

Healthstar Publications
P.O. Box 8426
Columbus, Ohio 43201

Copyright© 1980 Curtis Lee Janeczek

First Printing — May, 1980
Second Printing — October, 1980
Third Printing — January, 1981
Fourth Printing — May, 1981

The contents of this book do not necessarily reflect the views or the
sponsorship of The Ohio State University or The Ohio State University College of Medicine. Rather, they reflect the current thinking of
Mr. Janeczek on the subject. Mr. Janeczek is the sole proprietor and
author of this book and as such, holds all copyrights.

Library of Congress Catalog Card Number 80-81783

Printed at Lawhead Press, Inc., Columbus, Ohio. Edited by Jan Hall

In Dedication

To the Great Law-Giver, the unseen hand who guides us all.

And to my mother, Irene Janeczek, who has lovingly performed beyond the call of duty in raising a most difficult child.

And to my late father, Stephen Janeczek, who taught me courage and joy in the face of adversity.

TABLE OF CONTENTS

Thanks! viii
About the Author/About the Illustrator xi
How to Use this Book xii
Foreword by Robert L. DuPont, M.D. xiii

SECTION A: Background Thoughts/some things that need to be mentioned before jumping into a pile of facts

Letters to Important People 2
An Introduction to the Marijuana Story 7

SECTION B: Understanding Grass/the people, the scene, the medical story

You Wanna Get High? 10
It's a Matter of Chemistry 20
Marijuana and the Lungs 25
Marijuana and the Brain 30
How about a Contact High? 39
Dope and Driving 41
Grass and Reproduction 43
Grass, Genes, and Chromosomes 51
Marijuana and Immunity 55
Can You Get Hooked? 58
In Search of the Perfect Study 65

SECTION C: Putting It All Together/decisions along the road to better
      health

A Debate 74
Making Use of the Facts 76
Summary 87
Passing the Word 92
What Does Dope Have in Common with Junk Food,
Beer Bellies, and Tobacco Stains? 95
Closing Comments 100
Other Good Books on the Subject 101

APPENDIX: What's Normal for NORML? 103
Glossary of Dope Terms 111
Study Notes 115
References 129

Thanks!

Almost everything we do requires the kind help of others; this book is no exception.

Were it not for the folks who took an interest and helped keep this project moving. *Marijuana — Time for a Closer Look* would have been just another good idea that didn't quite make it. The way it turned out, some of the littlest suggestions and comments grew into important parts of the book. And those who offered major portions of their time and energies were like the sturdy mast upon which the flag flies.

I want to mention a few people separately. To say that anybody helped *the most* would be unfair to all the other wonderful souls who pitched in. But these folks definitely helped *a lot:*

Jeptha R. Hostetler, Ph.D., career teacher in substance abuse, Ohio State University, College of Medicine; Daniel Couri, M.D., Ph.D., director of toxicology, Ohio State University; Mrs. Irene Janeczek; Daniel H. Duffy; D.C. and Cecilia Duffy: Barry and Kay Hartman; Ann Schreck; Marnie Morrison; Jan Hall; Don Nichols, from Lawhead Press; John E. Hajar; Anne Taylor; Klaus Wiesmann.

I'd also like to mention the folks who helped in proofreading, who offered ideas for cartoons or essays, who provided technical expertise, who carted me across town when my Corolla wouldn't crank, and who otherwise made the preparing of this book a joy:

The kind souls at The Ohio State University, Department of Preventive Medicine, Martin D. Keller, M.D., Ph.D., chairman; Geraldine Keller, Ph.D., Franklin R. Banks, Ph.D., Mike Marchetto, Mary "Sis" Uhor. Also: Jeffrey M. Dicke, M.D., Jan Dicke, Steve Janeczek, my bro'; my sister, Denise Janeczek, Melanie Powell, Debra Jaynes, Maria Rusoff, Richard Rice, Brenda Johnson, Daniel Teeter, Weldon Kefauver, Uncle Andy, Aunt Joann, Mike and Barbie; Uncle Wally, Aunt Francie, Marie, Walt, Cathy, Rosemary, Jennifer; Tina Baughman, Fran Baughman, John Favret from BUDA; Cindy Squires, Vivian Schaefer, and Karen Luhring from the Health Sciences Library. In addition: Patrick "you asked for it, you got it" Stewart, Pat Podpadec and brother Yorta, Peggy Fadley, Norma Singer, Lois Hungate, Laurie Healy, Chuck Shelly, Jim Dasbach, Laura Leeson, Royse Brown, Grace Johnson, Alyn Massey, Linda Thomas, Jeanne Mangano-Roe, Ken Roe, Tim O'Neill, Teresa Lewis, Max Taubert, Doug Ungers, Bill "Casey Stengel" Baldner, Mary McGovern, Barbara Dill, Greg Paxton, Donna Distel, Cliff Lewis, Catherine Eckstrum, Thomas Lorance, M.D., Ralph Yaney, M.D., Nancy Johnson, Alexandros Genis, and Timothy Connors; and to all the bright lights who helped make this message possible and somehow didn't get listed, you are still listed in my heart.

I also want to thank the following scientists and experts who provided me with books, scientific articles, testimonies, and other valuable information:

Gabriel G. Nahas, M.D., Ph.D., College of Physicians and Surgeons, Columbia University; Robert DuPont, M.D., P.A.: Monique C. Braude, Ph.D., National Institute of Drug Abuse; Henry Brill, M.D.; Robert Gilkeson, M.D.; Susan Dalterio, Ph.D., University of Texas, Health Science Center; Ethyl N. Sassenrath, Ph.D., University of California; Carlton E. Turner, Ph.D., University of Mississippi; Austin T. Fitzjarrell, Ph.D., Tulane University School of Medicine; Akira Morishima, M.D., Ph.D., Columbia University; Robert Kolodny, M.D., Masters & Johnson Institute; David Martin, Peggy Mann, Barbara Dalrymple.

We owe these and many others a hand of applause for leading the way toward an honest scientific understanding of the health effects of marijuana.

Last but not least: My deepest appreciation to George Washington, Abe Lincoln, Uncle Sam, Lady Liberty, Old Glory, and all that is strong, proper, and worthy of respect in the American Heritage. A tip of the hat to Ludwig van Beethoven, for writing my all-time favorite background music. I also want to say "Hi" to all the wonderful friends and family I am fortunate enough to have. Hello to all the Janeczeks, Brestowskis, and other assorted relatives. Hello everybody in Madison, Columbus, Toledo, Dayton, Springfield, and Bellbrook, Ohio, and everyone back in the Greater Hazelton, Pennsylvania area. Since it would take half the book to individually thank each of you, just let me say I love you all.

About the Author

Curtis Lee Janeczek is a senior-year student at Ohio State University College of Medicine. He graduated *summa cum laude* with a BS in biology from Toledo University. Mr. Janeczek's areas of interest include trace mineral metabolism, exercise physiology, and preventive medicine, with special emphasis on nutrition. He believes patient education is the key to effective health care. He plans to enter family practice.

About the Illustrator

Ann L. Schreck, a professional medical illustrator, is a graduate student at Ohio State University. She has done work on medical books, journals, brochures, and slide presentations. She recently illustrated a book for nurse practitioners. After finishing a doctoral degree in medical communication, she plans to combine a career in medical illustration and education.

How To Use
This Book

To get the most out of this book, just read and think about the words, and laugh at the funny pictures. That's all there is to it.

I also want to mention the way this book is set up. It's divided into three sections, A, B, and C. In addition, at the end of the book there's a glossary of dope terms and some other information.

The middle section, B, contains most of the scientific facts about marijuana's health effects. It's the section that probably will be the most valuable to many young people. (It has the best cartoons!) So a young person who doesn't like to read much should start at section B.

But the marijuana story is not complete with just the medical facts. Added to the scientific complexities are social and personal questions that are even more imposing, more basic, more immediate. That's why sections A and C have been included. They provide important food for thought; they help readers understand the complicated issues that go along with marijuana's health effects.

Foreword

Marijuana: Time for a Closer Look is an important new book. It brings together for the first time the vital, new information about the health hazards of marijuana use for a youthful audience in a format which appeals to youth. This appeal is enhanced by the author's own youth, which adds significantly to his relevance. His status as a medical student lends important credibility to his work.

In reading and re-reading this book, I have found it to be accurate, informative and interesting. While it will not stop every reader from smoking marijuana, it will, I hope, convince even the most skeptical smokers that using pot is a serious health danger. This single point, beyond any others, has not yet gotten through to our youth (and to many who are no longer so young!) Reading this book will, finally, remove the last excuse for not recognizing the dangers posed by this, the most serious health problem now facing America's youth — and their parents.

When one out of nine high school seniors smokes marijuana every single day of his senior year, and when that rate doubled in just three years (to nearly twice the rate of daily use of alcohol in this group) then we truly do have a national epidemic of unprecedented proportions. One book won't turn around the trend to increasing marijuana use, but this book will surely make an important contribution to that vital goal.

Robert L. DuPont, M.D.

Chairman, World
Psychiatric Association's
drug-dependency section

Director of the National
Institute on Drug
Abuse, 1973-1978.

Background Thoughts

some things
that need to
be mentioned
before jumping
into a pile
of facts

Letters to Important People

Dear Student

This first letter is addressed to you. You are the star of this book. It is written both for you and about you.

Pot smoking among teenagers has increased faster than among any other age group. Almost twice as many of you now get high daily, compared to three years ago. So you probably need honest information more than anyone else.

You don't need someone pointing at you, saying, "You smoke grass so you must be some kind of bum." And you don't need someone cramming facts down your throat that you can hardly understand. If you cannot make sense out of the facts, how can you possibly expect to use them? That is why this book explains all the facts in everyday language. It helps you understand why this subject is worth thinking about. It puts the latest medical facts about marijuana out on the table for you to consider, without trying to blow things out of proportion.

I am not trying to freak anybody out. It would not make any sense to say you are going to "croak if you toke." Those of you who have smoked pot know that this is not true. But I do want you to know that there are many new studies that show pot may damage the lungs, the brain, and other body systems. For the most part, this damage doesn't happen overnight, and it won't happen to everybody who smokes.

Still, just because you can get out of bed the next day, it does not mean marijuana cannot wear you down, little by little. Remember that it often takes twenty years or more to get cancer.

But not all cigarette smokers will get lung cancer. We all have different types of bodies. We all have different strengths and different weaknesses. It is hard to predict who will get sick out of a group of people.

Take the example of heavy drinkers. Heavy drinking causes liver disease. If you studied a large number of drinkers for twenty years, some would die from liver damage. But it's not always the small fry. Sometimes the big strong guys go down first. I think it's Mother Nature's way of saying "Don't press your luck."

Let's say you're playing baseball. You get a single into the outfield and make it easily to first base. But you decide to keep running and try to make second base. The rules allow you to go for it. And you may make it to second, but you may not. Chances are, you're pressing your luck. Just remember, the umpire doesn't play favorites in enforcing the rules.

Just as the impartial umpire *enforces* the rules of baseball, nature *enforces* the laws of health. And just like baseball, there are certain laws of health we just can't buck. If we keep pounding away at the body long enough, it will break down.

How much wear and tear grass puts on the body, then, is what you need to read about in this book. Hopefully, by reading through it, you will be able to intelligently decide whether smoking pot is really worth it for you.

The next two letters are to your parents and teachers. Remember, you're not alone in this thing. Many parents are knocking their heads against the wall trying to figure out their kids. Most parents grew up before anyone ever heard of pot. They want to understand their children, and they want to know the story on marijuana. Teachers also have a tough job. They're supposed to help prepare you to step into the "adult world." Let's face it, you are the next generation.

In other words, everybody's trying to figure out what's the best thing to do. Parents and teachers need the facts as much as you do.

Before you go to section B on the latest medical findings, you might want to read the letters to parents and teachers. Try to understand their side. After all, they do play a pretty big part in your lives.

Dear Parents

This book has been written with the junior high school and high school student in mind. However, the medical facts will be interesting to anyone of any age.

This book will help to bridge the generation gap on the subject of marijuana. If you take the time to read and think about this book, you'll better understand the special pressures and influences on modern teens. Marijuana is not only a medical issue, it's a social one. It's a part of teen life that has become very common in today's world.

The banner of "Smoke grass, don't mow it" is a new flag waved by this generation. The rise in marijuana use was a phenomenon of the 1960s, a time of many new twists in behavior. For some, grass was and still is a symbol of rebellion against authority, including parents. As such, in many families the subject has caused a considerable breakdown of communication between parents and children.

This book will expose some of the myths about marijuana, giving a comprehensive review of current medical literature. Informed scientists now think the drug may present risks for even the casual user. But the mere fact that dope is bad for the body doesn't make someone who smokes it a bad person.

Remember that the family unit weaves the very fabric of our society. Thus, it is important to use information about grass in a way that won't cause an increase in conflicts at home. Hopefully, there won't be any "I told you so" campaigns waged against youth who never heard any of this stuff.

Realize that your teenagers, like everyone else, must make up their own minds about pot — and about the world. Even the most watchful parent can't keep tabs on their kids twenty-four hours a day.

This is not to undermine the role of parents. Though I can't speak firsthand, I feel being a parent is one of the greatest responsibilities anywhere. It's truly one of the most complicated. When communication is good among family members, it can make all the hassles of a parent worthwhile.

Before gearing up for an assault on your children's marijuana habits, reflect a moment on your own unwanted habits. Whether it's cigarettes, laziness, or excess food, tube, or booze, chances are good these habits are fueled by similar weaknesses. Insecurity, tension, doubt, fears, or peer pressure underlie most all unwanted habit patterns — young and old alike.

With many teens today, then, right or wrong, marijuana use is probably part of a search. Perhaps it's not unlike your own quest for identity, security, and happiness, except you've been at it longer.

So instead of using this book as ammunition against the kids, use it to bring your family closer together. By honestly discussing marijuana, this potential stumbling-block to family unity can be turned into a stepping stone. Place this difficult and important topic out in the open, and your family might grow to understand each other better.

Dear Teachers

How do we teach a science barely graduated past infancy? Well, while the complex picture of Cannabis use and human health is still young, the state of the art is sufficiently advanced so that clear statements can now be made in many areas. Furthermore, the swift upsurge in marijuana  use dictates that any pertinent findings must be taught.

We must address the needs of those involved, those who deserve to know what they've gotten into. And the other group, those presently not involved, face an even more acute need for instruction on marijuana.

For the problem is not only medical, but environmental. The prevailing winds of mass behavior exert a pressure on the teen to *DO THIS THING* — to smoke pot. The question now becomes, how can teachers help students make up thier own minds instead of going along with the crowd? Especially those students who wouldn't get involved except for the fact that everyone else is doing it. What do we owe these students, who deserve the best our schools can offer?

At the minimum, we can present the facts. For at minimum, they will be offered marijuana by their friends.

From a societal and global viewpoint, the problems of life have spiraled to new heights of complexity. Today, then, passing the torch of civilization's leadership to the youth was perhaps never more critical. As always, hopes for future solutions to present dilemmas rest with the talents of the upcoming generation.

The urgency for leadership is complicated by this fact: over one-ninth of all high school seniors smoke pot daily. Yet the public now believes that marijuana poses no greater threat than alcohol or tobacco.

Upon what is this belief based? If it is based upon outdated assumptions, unqualified opinions, and premature or reckless conclusions, we may indeed be in for a surprise! What if marijuana is conclusively proven more damaging to health, especially the brain, than alcohol or cigarettes? A huge segment of the next generation could be adversely affected.

Where would the future leaders in government, science and the arts come from? While most marijuana users, even long-term users, seem to function with relative proficiency, there are definite warning signs that the brain can be permanently harmed. The motive of this speculation, then, is to identify a potentially 'endangered species.' I am referring to the species called 'genius,' a rare breed we cannot afford to lose.

Can educators view the rapid upsurge in marijuana use with passive interest? Considering the expected role of schools in providing useful education, I think not! Teachers must make every effort to become informed as to what the medical risks of marijuana use are.

This book is designed to serve as an interim measure (a catalyst, if you will) to spur interest and the confidence that all teachers can grasp the basic dynamics of the issue, and that a realistic understanding of pot can be effectively communicated to youth.

So you're hereby challenged to get actively involved in cultivating attitudes about marijuana based on facts — not folklore, wistful ignorance, or denial of reality.

An Introduction to the Marijuana Story

What are the important things to consider when talking about marijuana?

Let's begin with the obvious. Are there really any issues to consider? Is the marijuana question worth talking about? The answer is yes, because more people than ever are now smoking grass.

Over three-fifths of high school seniors have tried marijuana. Government estimates show that in the last five years, the number of teenagers smoking dope daily has almost doubled. In addition, the grass being sold today is far stronger than ever before.

The next thing to consider when talking about grass is that it's a very complicated issue. The marijuana problem isn't just something interesting to research in the laboratory; it is a loaded question. Because marijuana has such a broad impact on society, emotions tend to "ride high" when speaking about marijuana.

Some people consider it a part of their life. When they hear someone talking about the marijuana problem, they think he's either "for" or "against" pot smokers. But isn't it possible for someone to be "pro-truth" about marijuana without being "for" this law or "against" that attitude? Scientists are certainly not fanatics just because they speak out about marijuana's health effects. But grass is such an emotional issue that these medical effects are often ignored.

What else should we consider about the topic of grass? Obviously, we must keep *reason* in mind when talking about it. Extremes are not helpful. We know that family members shouldn't stop talking to each other. We know that harsh penalties for possessing small quantities show insensitivity to the real people involved.

On the other side, we can't pretend everything's just fine when the facts prove otherwise. To deny that there's a problem is the "ostrich-in-the-sand" approach, which is just as insensitive to the needs of teenagers. (You can't find answers when you hide from the questions!) The middle

road, the road of reason, is the only logical way to discuss the marijuana issue.

There's one more thing to consider when talking about grass. Medical research has, for several years, been gathering solid evidence that marijuana interferes with how the body works. However, *scientists often disagree* and the research *is pretty technical*. For these two reasons, students and parents don't really know much about the new discoveries. They can't really make a wise decision about marijuana because all they know now is a blend of truth, half-truths, folklore, and pure baloney. But they want to know the facts.

This book, *Marijuana, Time for a Closer Look,* will help you understand what grass is all about. It will talk about the medical, social, and personal issues in a variety of ways. Then *you* have to participate and think about what you've read.

As you read, you'll probably find terms you're not familiar with. A glossary at the end of the book will clue you in to some current marijuana slang.

Are you ready to find out what the real story is? Read on and be prepared to make up your own mind.

Understanding Grass

the people,
the scene,
the medical
story

You Wanna Get High?

Has anyone ever asked you to get high? Did they say, "Come on, you'll like it. And it's not bad for you at all."

You know, twenty years ago people said smoking cigarettes was harmless, too, but now we know it causes lung cancer and heart disease. Today some people say grass is no worse than alcohol or cigarettes.

It may take another twenty years before we understand *exactly* how grass affects health. But hundreds of studies come out every year with important findings. These facts are beginning to add up.

Scientists now know grass affects many parts of the body. For instance, it interferes with cell growth. The chemicals in grass stay in the body for weeks, causing stress. It is thought that they may weaken a person's defenses against disease.

What chemicals are in grass? Unlike alcohol, which has only one chemical, pot has hundreds.[a] The most-studied part of pot is THC, short for *tetrahydrocanabinol*. Scientists still have much to find out about the other chemicals in pot.

What is this Rap Anyway?

You've noticed this isn't an ordinary textbook. This is a rap about grass — what researchers know and what their studies mean.

The Facts are Only Part of It

The marijuana question involves millions of people. It involves you, too — what you like, what you need, what you think about, where you're going, your friends, your family, your life.

A Challenge

Advertisers often ask you to prove you're tough enough to "take" what they're selling. Fast food chains dare you to tackle their hefty burgers. Car dealers challenge you to find a better ride. The Marines say they want a "few good men."

Well, everybody, there's no sales pitch here. This book doesn't offer any products to buy, no clubs to join. But here is a challenge:

Read this Book!

Your challenge is to read this book. Of course nobody can make you do anything.

But whether you're straight or smoke ten joints a day, there's stuff in here you'll want to know. As you read, you'll have to ask yourself some questions. If you're tough enough to handle it, proceed with caution.

Who Smokes Pot?

Lots of people smoke it. Tokers come in all ages and from all parts of the country. One out of every four Americans has gotten stoned at least once. Most people who smoke are between twelve and thirty-five, but quite a few grannies have been known to roll a joint.[b]

More people smoke now than used to. Look at this next graph showing that in the last four years, the number of smokers in the senior class (daily users) has just about doubled.

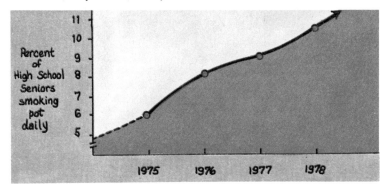

As you can see from the graph, one out of nine seniors smoke pot daily.[c] What the graph doesn't show is that three out of five have at least tried dope and one out of three smokes at least once a month.

Studies also show that there are many young users. Almost half of all high schoolers smoking grass started before or during junior high.

And think about the money all these people spend on grass! Each year Americans convert over $20 billion dollars into marijuana smoke. You could buy General Motors, the world's largest car maker, for less than that.

Another Sign of the Times — Stronger Pot

More people than ever are getting stoned, and they're smoking *stronger* pot than ever before.

Scientists measure the strength of marijuana by testing how much THC it contains. THC is pot's main chemical, the ingredient that gives tokers the high.[d]

During the 1960s, the average pot smoked in the United States had less than one percent THC. An average joint first creeped above one percent THC during the early 1970s. It stayed around one percent until around 1975, when much more potent pot began to get smuggled into the country.

From about 1975, street reefer has shot upward in strength. A typical joint now contains over four percent THC. In fact, government figures show that average street pot now has *more THC than average hashish*. Powerful stuff! This graph shows how joints have been growing in potency.[e]

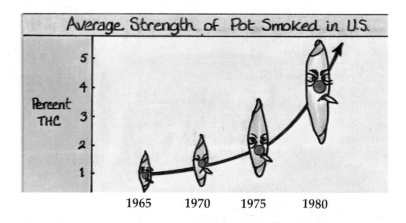

Why do People Smoke Dope?

You can probably think of plenty of reasons. For example, Marti said she was curious the first time. Dan said he wanted to go along with the crowd.

In fact, research shows peer pressure (wanting to be part of the crowd) is the most likely reason people start using grass.

Are *You* Cool?

"Are you cool? Is she cool? Don't worry, you're both okay." You know, *cool* doesn't mean the same thing it used to, especially in high school. A cool person used to be someone everybody liked. But now many people call a person cool just because he or she smokes dope. He may have a mean temper and she may be selfish, but it doesn't matter. If they get high, they're still "cool."

And talk about discrimination! Sometimes folks who choose not to smoke grass are considered part of the "out crowd," even if they're friendly and active in school. *Square* or *straight* often mean a non-smoker doesn't quite measure up. Do people really need dope to be cool?

Escape, Anyone?

Everybody's got problems. Sometimes the pressures from home, school, or job really build up. We all need ways of getting out of the rat-race, Some people choose movies, reading, working, sports, quiet meditation, or walking in the park. But are these the same kinds of escapes provided by marijuana, booze, or other drugs?

You Can't Hide from Yourself

Common sense says that not even the strongest drug can tell you something you don't already know. It's also true that after the drug wears off, the same old problems are still hanging around — if you haven't created some new mess while buzzed out of your mind.

Each problem not faced adds to the stack against you. The unhappy lives of most alcoholics proves this point. Could this be a hint that drugs are a dead-end street, leading every which way but out?

What about Dope for Fun and Profit?

Okay, you say none of these reasons you've just read about is your reason. You're just smoking because you like it. Everything goes better with a good joint or a couple of bongs. You say it hasn't affected how you get along with others and the way you look at life. You say you feel pretty good, still have a good memory, and can concentrate well enough. You say you don't feel burnt out. No cough, no paranoid feelings, no thoughts that lately your problems seem larger or harder to solve.

Of course it's your decision. You've got your own life to lead. If you think pot lights up your life, it's easy enough to find. And only dealers get busted nowadays. But are you *really* sure about how worthwhile pot is?

What's the Price?

About $40 a bag. But there's another price — the wear and tear on your body — and for some, that price can be steep.

"Oh," you say, "some studies show grass is harmless." Forget it! Those studies probably are dated in the late 1960s and early 1970s. (Check it out for yourself.) In medical research, especially with marijuana, those days are like the Stone Age.

True, not all the facts are in yet. But what's already been discovered might surprise you.

Ask the Experts

With any subject, to get the facts you've got to ask the experts. To get the facts on grass, you've got to ask the doctors and scientists in the labs seriously studying the question.

Look at it this way. Can you expect to find that kind of reliable information in the latest issue of *High Times?*[f] It's not impossible, but I wouldn't count on it.

Check It Out!

In this book I describe the experiments that tell us the most about grass. (There sure are a lot of experiments!) You can go to the library and read about all this stuff. Most of the magazines and books I used are listed in the reference sections at the end of this book. The footnote numbers you'll see while reading each refer to a source in the reference lists.

You can ignore these footnotes if you want. But if you find a topic you're interested in, look up the footnote number and talk to your teacher or librarian about finding the original information.

Some of you will want more details on the scientific studies. The small footnote letters will refer you to the "study notes" section in the back of the book, where you'll find further information. Don't take my word for it — be curious!

A Note about THC

This book will discuss experiments where THC is given to people or animals. THC is pot's main chemical. In its pure form, THC can *only* be handled under very strict laboratory conditions. Real THC is *never* sold on the street.

I mention this to avoid confusion with a street drug often called "THC" or *angel dust*. This drug is usually an impure blend containing PCP (it is *never* THC). Doctors call PCP one of the most violent and destructive street drugs known. (Since PCP is cheap and easy for back-alley chemists to make, it's also very common.)

PCP can tear your body up almost as badly as gasoline or drain cleaner. Unfortunately, many young people have proven this fact. So if someone offers you "THC," *don't* be fooled. It *won't* be THC; more than likely, it *will* be trouble.[8]

√

It's a Matter
of Chemistry

What's in Marijuana?

The chemical in grass that makes people high is called THC. But there are other chemicals in grass that may affect the body even more powerfully than THC (but no one is sure how).

Stranger yet, marijuana "tells" the body to make new chemicals on its own. So in addition to what's in marijuana, the lungs and the liver make more chemicals.[a] No one knows yet how these organs become changed in the way they work.

It is known, though, that dopers breathe in tar and pollutants from the burning papers. Some people even use more paper in joints than in cigarettes. In cigarettes, these ingredients cause lung cancer. It is possible that joints cause cancer, too.

What Does the Body Do with this Stuff?

Guess what? This is a hard question! But scientists know quite a lot about it.

For starters, the way the body uses up grass is nothing like the way it uses up alcohol. Whereas alcohol leaves the body right away, grass stays in the body a long time.

That's because a drink (wine, beer, liquor) is used up as fuel by the body very quickly. Six hours after having a drink, your body has burned it all up.[b]

But what happens after using grass? A pot smoker will feel a buzz soon after toking up, usually within a minute. The high will be gone in a few hours. That may be the end of the fun, but it's not the end of the chemistry!

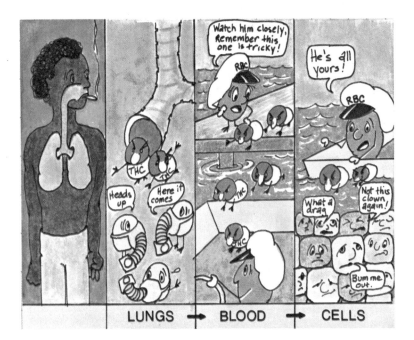

When dope's chemicals get into the blood, some of them are changed by the lungs and the liver.[1] The main chemical in pot is THC. Some of it gets broken down into other chemicals that don't give a high.[2] The rest of the THC is stored in the cells.

THC is pretty interesting. It's a lot like an insecticide, DDT, in how it works. THC loves fat![3,c] It flows toward fat like moths to a light bulb. It hurries to get from the blood to inside cells that are rich in fat.[d] It ends up in brain cells, the liver, lungs, kidneys, and glands.[4,5,6,7] It gets locked up

in the cells and tends to stay there for a long time.[8]

That's when a smoker loses the buzz but doesn't lose the dope. Results from experiments vary, but most show it takes several weeks to more than a month for the body to get rid of dope's chemicals.[3,7,9] In recent experiments on dogs, it took a whole month to clear out the THC *from only one joint.*[9]

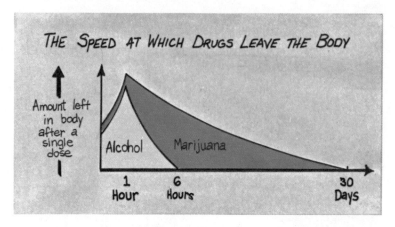

So one week after smoking a joint, the body has almost half the dope left. If someone just smokes on weekends, she or he still has dope in the body all week. For heavy users, the chemicals build up. Someone who smokes every day probably has ten times as much dope in his body as someone who rarely smokes.[7,e]

It's easy to see now what the body does with this stuff — it keeps it!

But Does It Hurt Anybody?

We're leading up to that. First, however, you must know a little about what it means to "prove" what harm marijuana can do. Most of what we know about marijuana comes from laboratories all around the world. Scientists study what pot does to test animals, like rats, mice, dogs, and monkeys. They also study cells from the blood, the lungs, and the muscles. From these studies, there is a lot known about pot's effects. But there is a catch!

A person is not a rat, or a dog, or a cell in a test dish. For example, pregnant rats who breathe marijuana smoke have small and sickly babies, when their babies survive at all. But that doesn't automatically prove the same thing would happen to a human.

Results of tests on monkeys, which are more like people than rats, are more important. Still, people aren't exactly like monkeys, either.

Humans, on the other hand, are hard to study. They don't like to sit in a cage for six months, or a year, or longer. That means you can't control their diet or their exercise, or any of the things that help prove things scientifically.

What you have to do, then, is study large numbers of people. If you are studying dope, you find about a hundred people who smoke it, and you run tests. Even this method is not perfect.

There have been quite a few studies on real, live people, though. More are being done, and many others are on the drawing board. But for each person, there are a few trillion cells, which is also a few million-million cells. And most every cell agrees:

Cells Don't Like Pot!

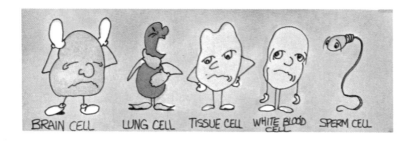

BRAIN CELL   LUNG CELL   TISSUE CELL   WHITE BLOOD CELL   SPERM CELL

Like it says on top of the picture, CELLS DON'T LIKE POT! Period! This is probably the best known scientific fact known about the stuff. Anyone who has read even a few scientific articles knows it to be true.

Marijuana is poison to cells! Dozens of experiments have proven it over and over again. In almost any kind of cell, pot messes up cell growth and cell division.[10-14] That goes for lung cells, blood cells, sperm cells, brain cells, human cells, and rabbit cells.

Pot prevents the proper formation of *DNA, RNA,* and *proteins.* These are building blocks for cell growth and cell division. Studies show that cells "under the influence" often don't split apart to make new cells correctly.[15-19]

In the lab, scientists treat cells with THC or marijuana extract. Sometimes these cells turn out to have too many or too few *chromosomes,* the code for making new cells. When chromosomes are screwed up, mutations, or cancer can result. By the way, changes can occur with only small amounts of dope — amounts that ordinary pot-smokers can have in their bodies.[f]

If this stuff about pot messing up your cells sounds heavy, that means you're thinking! And it is pretty heavy — especially when most of the people smoking dope believe they can toke all they want, without any sort of danger. But believe this: You will hear more and more of this type of information, as medical research discovers more and more answers.

Still, let's not blow things out of proportion. You see, not all scientists agree what this means for real people. They know what happens when grass chemicals are added to cells or tissue slices, then grown in a test dish. They also know cells in a laboratory can act differently from cells still in the body.

And it's true. You cannot always predict what will happen in a person, from experiments with isolated cells. But it can give a good idea of what might be going on — that cells don't like pot!

Enough about cells! We will come back to some of these topics later. Now we're going to talk about something big. Lungs are pretty big; let's talk about lungs.

* * * * *

In the next few sections, I'll be not only talking about lungs but also about how grass affects other parts of the body. Here's a list of what you can expect to learn about:

1. the lungs
2. the brain
3. contact highs
4. driving skills
5. reproduction

6. genes and chromosomes
7. immunity
8. getting hooked
9. a famous study
10. glossary of dope terms

Marijuana
and the Lungs

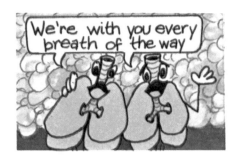

We know a lot more than we used to about what pot does to the lungs. It's becoming common knowledge — smoking dope can do a number on your "windbags."

Recent tests show pot may be worse on your lungs than cigarettes. For example, if you smoke two to ten joints a day, you will probably show mild signs of lung trouble after less than two months. Fortunately, tests also show that if smoking is stopped, most harmful lung changes eventually return to normal.

Here's a list of the recent discoveries I'm going to talk about in detail:

1. Dope smokers can't breathe as well.
2. Dope smoke damages the insides of the lungs.
3. Damage can be permanent.
4. Dope could cause lung cancer, like cigarettes.
5. Marijuana smoke weakens the lung's ability to fight off disease.
6. An important clue that marijuana causes cancer.
7. Hashish damages the breathing tubes, causing abnormal tissue of the type found in heavy-cigarette-smoking adults.
8. X-ray tests aren't good enough to show early lung damage caused by smoking grass.

Dopers can't breathe as well.

One college tested seventeen healthy males. They were told to smoke all the dope they wanted. On the average, each smoked over four joints per day. (They weren't allowed to drink or smoke cigarettes.)

When the study began, all had normal lungs. After seven weeks, every subject couldn't breathe as well. When they tried to blow air out of their lungs, they couldn't do it as fast as they could before they started smoking grass.[1,a] This is considered an early sign of lung trouble.

Several other tests run on these subjects also suggested that heavy pot smoking causes a narrowing of the breathing passages. At least in the early stages of dope smoking, these changes clear up after smoking is stopped.

However, there is pretty good evidence that pot can cause *permanent* lung damage. Scientists don't yet agree how serious this is, but are studying the question very intensely.

When dope smoke changes the insides of the lungs, damage can be permanent.

One study exposed 340 rats to one to six joints a day for one year. (That is, small amounts equal to from one to six joints for a person.) At the end of that time, the rats' breathing tubes showed severe inflammation and their lungs showed areas of destroyed tissue.[2,b]

Only in the rats given low doses of THC did the serious changes go back to anywhere near normal. This dose equalled about one joint per day of good quality reefer. But the rest of the rats' lungs remained damaged, even after a month off of marijuana. Therefore, this lung damage was probably permanent. These results were found in a large number of the rats tested. From this experiment alone, it is very clear that marijuana can cause serious lung damage.

Dope could cause lung cancer, like cigarettes.

What if those rats had been exposed to marijuana smoke longer, say several years? Could they have gotten cancer? Because of what we know about cigarettes and cancer, the answer is probably *yes*.

Part of the job of scientists, is to use the information they have, and then put two plus two together. A very important piece of information concerns the smoke made when pot is burned. Chemical studies of this smoke have shown it to be quite nasty!

It contains over 150 different chemicals probably capable of causing cancer. One type of chemical, *hydrocarbons,* are proven to cause cancer. Dope smoke has a lot more hydrocarbons than tobacco smoke.[3,c]

So add it up. Cigarettes are the leading cause of lung cancer. A key reason for this is the hydrocarbons formed when cigarettes are burned. If marijuana smoke has more of these hydrocarbons than tobacco, do you really need to wait twenty-five years to be "sure" smoking marijuana can cause lung cancer?

By that time, there will probably be enough lung-cancer patients who smoked pot to conclusively "prove" marijuana causes cancer in humans. But you need to look at thousands of people. In so many words, it is a matter of *statistics: when the numbers are large enough, the numbers don't lie.*

Statistics are how we know cigarettes cause cancer. The numbers are so overwhelming, not even tobacco companies bother to argue with them. Instead, tobacco companies (like most advertisers) use ads to play with people's minds. The ads try to make you believe you need cigarettes to survive and be popular with the opposite sex. How come the smoker in the ad never lights up in the cancer ward? Instead, the guy is either smiling on a horse or splashing in a swimming pool.

There are still questions to be answered. But scientists already know plenty about marijuana and the lungs. With the facts presently in hand, it doesn't take much imagination to know dope can cause cancer of the lungs. Proof is only a matter of time.

Even if pot smoke does have more cancer-causing agents than tobacco smoke, is that such a big deal? After all, many cigarette smokers puff through two or three dozen cancer-sticks daily. Not even a heavy burner goes through that much pot.

Indeed, hardly anyone smokes a "pack" of joints each day. But think about these ideas:

1. How many cigarette smokers hold the smoke in for ten or twenty seconds after they inhale? Deep and long toking of marijuana allows more time for harmful particles and gases to act on the lung cells.[4,d]

2. Most pot smokers use more paper in rolling doobies than you find in cigarettes. Burning paper makes chemicals that irritate the lungs.[e]

3. More marijuana chemicals end up in lung tissues than in many other body parts. They're strongly "attracted" to lungs.[5,6,f]

Marijuana smoke weakens the lung's ability to fight off disease.

The lung has special cells to destroy disease-producing bacteria. For at least six hours after smoking a joint, they don't do their job as well.[7,8] Dope smokers, then, may be more likely to catch an infection from bacteria they breathe in.

An important clue that marijuana causes cancer.

Swiss researchers exposed over 5,000 samples of lung tissue (from mice, hamsters, and humans) to tobacco and marijuana smoke. Three days a week, each tissue got a "toke." After only thirty-five weeks, cancerous changes clearly occurred, and the damage was worst in lung tissue exposed to marijuana.[8] Remember these are only test cells in a dish — but it's an important clue.

Hashish damages the breathing tubes, causing abnormal tissue.

Several studies have tested soldiers who smoked hashish, or *hash,* which is a more potent form of marijuana.[9, 10] Some soldiers had been smoking for six months, others for as long as two years. Hashish was found to irritate their lungs, and was clearly associated with bronchitis and asthma.[h] The soldiers coughed, had sore throats, and wheezed. Doctors found that soldiers who volunteered for extensive testing had abnormal tissue in their bronchial (breathing) tubes. One had changes that were the step just before full-blown cancer starts to grow.[9]

    The doctors who ran these tests made an interesting observation. They said they had seen these problems only in older people who smoked cigarettes a lot. But these soldiers were aged nineteen to twenty-two!

X-ray tests aren't good enough to show early lung damage caused by smoking grass.

Some studies have not found evidence that smoking pot is especially harmful to the lungs.[11] Most of these, however, did not use the kind of detailed tests many doctors feel are needed to detect *early* marijuana-related lung damage. X-rays, for example, have been commonly used to check for lung damage due to marijuana. It turns out, however, that x-rays aren't very reliable for this purpose. They're not reliable in picking out problems related to marijuana. Early detection of damage requires more detailed testing.[i]

Smoking is smoking!

You know, some people have a really amazing attitude about smoking dope. They don't think it's "real smoking," like smoking cigarettes. Scientists today say — Your lungs know no difference!

Marijuana and the Brain

The brain is harder to study than other parts of the body. This incredible organ is still pretty much a mystery to modern scientists.

Especially baffling is the process of thinking. Scientists know that brain waves follow pathways inside the head, but they can't really tell you how we think. They know that memory involves protein, DNA, RNA, and certain areas deep within the brain. How memory works, though, is not fully understood.

Personality is another big mystery — our emotions, attitudes, how we act and speak. How does all that fit in with what we know about the chemistry and structure of the brain?

All these unanswered questions make the study of how marijuana affects the brain very challenging. The complexity of the brain even surpasses the complexity of trying to figure out what pot can do to our thinking ability!

For years people have been worried that smoking grass might damage the brain. They thought that anything that could "mess your mind up" as much as pot would almost have to do some type of damage. But not everyone agreed with that, and people kept smoking, so scientists had to try to find out the truth.

Here's a list of the topics you'll be reading about next:

1. The shrinking brain theory.
2. THC stays in the brain because it loves fat.
3. Monkey junkies give us important clues.
4. The deep brain — a key area where dope does its thing.
5. THC changes brain waves in the areas that are most important to pleasure and emotion.
6. Surface recordings can't detect deep-brain damage.

7. THC changes brain cells in heavy smokers, even after six months of not smoking.
8. Grass may cause a disease of the emotions.
9. Walking, talking people are tough to study.
10. A new link between personality problems and abnormal brain waves.
11. Tests on overseas smokers show evidence of thinking difficulties.
12. Memory may suffer in dope smokers.

The shrinking brain theory.

In 1971 some researchers said the brain tissue of long-term, heavy users (three to eleven years) actually shrank.[1,a] Since then, however, other studies say brain size and shape stays the same.[2,3] To be able to tell any difference, though, the brain would have to change a great deal, and so far nothing that dramatic has been noticed. But the brain is so delicate that even a small change — undetected by looking at weight or size — could be harmful.

THC stays in the brain because it loves fat.

The brain has much fat in it. With repeated smoking, THC piles up in the brain.[5] As was said before, it hangs around much like the insecticide, DDT, and it tends to stay a while once it moves in.

Monkey junkies give us clues.

Dr. Robert Heath of Tulane University has studied how grass affects Rhesus monkeys (The monkeys most like humans). He and others have spent about ten years investigating what marijuana does to the brain.[b] They have used highly advanced methods and have come up with some interesting discoveries.

The deep brain — a key area where dope does its thing.

Dr. Heath is one of the world's leading experts on the areas deep within the brain. These areas can only be tested by special methods. They are locations that play a major part in maintaining our emotional health. They seem to be key areas where dope does its thing.[c]

THC changes brain waves in the areas that are most important to pleasure and emotion.

Rhesus monkeys were given (with a special helmet gadget) measured amounts of marijuana smoke. Some monkeys got one joint a day; others got three. The joints they smoked were much smaller than what people would smoke, but they were equal to a human dose. The monkeys got stoned for six months. During this time the scientists studied the monkeys' brain waves.

A test called the *EEG* was used in these experiments. The EEG is a recording of electronic waves made by the brain. In this series of tests, however, the recordings were not made in the usual manner (on the surface of the head.)

In these experiments, the recording monitors were surgically placed deep inside the monkeys' brains. Brain waves of the pleasure and emotion areas were clearly abnormal.[6,7] The scientific team said the brain wave damage lasted at least a month after the monkeys stopped smoking grass. They reported that permanent damage was a possibility.[7,d]

Surface recordings can't detect deep-brain damage.

Dr. Heath and company then placed the EEG recorders on the surface of the monkeys' heads. As we said before, this method is the run-of-the-mill brainwave test most people receive. In the same monkeys that had abnormal deep-brain waves, *the surface brain waves were perfectly normal.*[7]

This point could be very important. For if marijuana damages the deep parts of the brain, regular surface EEGs have little chance of measuring it. This is not to say that surface tests are worthless in detecting brain damage (only that deep-brain damage probably won't be found with this test.)

In fact, there have been important new breakthroughs in using surface brain wave tests to identify problems caused by pot (more on this shortly).[e] But Dr. Heath's work says that damage to deep-brain areas cannot be ruled out for human tokers. Several other studies have shown marijuana to act upon deep-brain areas.[8,9,10]

THC changes brain cells in heavy smokers, even after six months of not smoking.

Dr. Heath's research team has also studied the individual brain cells of monkeys who toke. For eight months, five days a week, the monkeys got a dose of THC equal to two joints a day for a person.

The deep-brain (pleasure and emotion) areas were viewed under an *electron microscope*. With this device, the tissues were magnified up to 80,000 times. (That's one whale of a magnifying glass!)

There was swelling and other changes in the parts of the cells where proteins are made. The empty spaces between the cells got bigger and "junk" collected in these spaces. Junk (cell garbage) also collected within the nucleus, which is the heart of each cell.[6,11,12,f]

THC was responsible for these changes. Even after two months without marijuana, the monkeys' brain cells still weren't back to normal. This study, then, provided the first solid evidence that marijuana can permanently change brain cells (for the worse).

Does grass cause disease of the emotions?

From Dr. Heath's work, it appears the very structure of the brain can change (at least in monkeys) from using marijuana. The brain areas dealing with emotions are one of the main targets of marijuana. Does that mean, then, pot smokers run a risk of "damaged" emotions? According to the medical research, it appears they do run such a risk.

We have examined brains for several pages now. These brains are probably getting tired of us doing all the talking. It is high time we let the brains speak for themselves.

Other studies also suggest that continued use of grass may harm the brain.

For example, rats treated with THC have also showed abnormal brain waves in deep-brain areas.[10] Infant rats given THC show fewer of the structures that make protein in the brain cells.[13] Making new protein, for example, is needed to remember things.

The brains of rats born to mothers given THC contain less protein than normal rats.[14] In unborn (fetal) mice, more THC goes to brain and nerve tissue than to any other body tissues.[15] Incidentally, a

mother who is stoned *automatically gives her unborn child marijuana chemicals.*[16]

Walking, talking people are tough to study.

The experiments just mentioned say that dope poses some threat to a person's good mental health. Unfortunately, there is no easy way of knowing what harm can come to walking, talking people. You can't just take out a human brain, slap it under a microscope and call it a "day's work" in medical research. So human brains often have to be studied by indirect methods, such as *psychological testing.*

Can dope make you crazy?

So, you can't inspect the brains of pot smokers. And the standard brain-wave tests are *just beginning* to show real promise in pot research.[e] Where do you go from there? You can still see if pot smokers show signs of mental problems. In other words, can dope make you crazy?

Before we talk about psychological testing and personality studies, I invite you to look for yourself. Take a close look at long-time potheads you know. Do they look burnt out? Are they crazy? To make it easy on your friends, maybe you should just come right out and ask them?

All kidding aside, many psychologists report that long-time smokers show a predictable pattern of difficulties. Enough professional "shrinks" have made similar observations that there truly appears to be a *marijuana syndrome.*

Marijuana syndrome — No laughing matter.

Trained professionals believe an alarming number of pot smokers change their personalities for the worse over the years. Common complaints from smokers (especially young smokers) include inability to remember details, loss of will power and motivation, and difficulty in concentrating.

One psychiatrist dramatically switched his views on pot during eight years as director of mental health services at a major university. From interviewing over a thousand students, Dr. Powelson became convinced that pot can result in clear mental damage. Many dopers told him they couldn't handle the same level of college work as before they started smoking. He also talked with mathematicians and others in advanced fields who personally felt marijuana had reduced their intellectual abilities.[17,18,g]

Doctors Kolansky and Moore have published several studies on long-time tokers. Their findings also support the belief that the personalities of pot smokers can change for the worse with continued pot use. From their experience in treating hundreds of marijuana smokers, they have found that poor memory, loss of willpower and motivation, poor ability to concentrate, and paranoia (a sense of fear) are the most common of doper complaints.[19,20] They have found that the younger the smoker, the more often these problems occur. Dr. Moore, along with several other psychiatrists, testified before the Senate in 1974. They all described similar problems in their patients who used marijuana.[21,22,23]

The medical literature is loaded with the trained observations of counselors, educators, and "shrinks" on the subject of marijuana. Almost every expert in these areas who has written a paper on grass mentions the same types of problems (poor memory, loss of willpower, apathy, paranoia, and distrust of others). One article lists over a hundred papers dealing with pot's harmful effects on the human psyche.[24]

On the other hand, some people have criticized marijuana findings reported by psychologists, psychiatrists, and educators. They argue that interviews with patients, even when the patients are treated for years, can't scientifically prove anything.

The thing is, the medical literature discusses thousands of patients with similar problems from marijuana. Could hundreds of trained professionals all be "biased" against pot? Could the "marijuana syndrome" be just a big hoax dreamed up by old fuddy-duddies who think dope's a drag? It doesn't look like it. In fact, almost everyone knows at least one person who has had problems keeping his or her head together after getting into the dope scene.

Fifteen thousand young people help prove the point.

During January 1980, Dr. Mitchell Rosenthal addressed the Senate on the subject of marijuana. Dr. Rosenthal is president of the Phoenix House Foundation, the nation's largest live-in program for the treatment of drug abuse. Phoenix House has helped almost 15,000 young men and women who felt drugs were ruining their lives.

According to Dr. Rosenthal, almost every patient who comes to Phoenix House has smoked pot. He also said that many of these troubled young people had never used hard drugs; marijuana alone caused them to seek help.

This expert in child psychiatry stated that grass is "at least as threatening to health as tobacco or alcohol." His greatest fear, however, is that pot may be able to stunt the mental and emotional growth of young people who make it part of their lives. From his experience with thousands of teenagers, he believes pot's most damaging effects are on behavior — "the impairment of judgment, memory or learning disability, and the loss of motivation, coordination, or motor skills."

Dr. Rosenthal thinks that pot tends to damage the emotional growth of regular users. He says it makes people less able to put aside momentary pleasures in order to get a firm grip on their problems. In other words, pot makes people less able to plan ahead and then carry out their plans.

He also stresses the fact that grass is being used by younger and younger people all the time: "Nearly one-third of all New York's seventh and eighth graders have already tried the drug." He feels the long-range effects on America could be very serious: "If the number of regular users and daily users continues to increase — then our nation is well on its way to acquiring an unmanageable number of emotionally or intellectually handicapped individuals."

Sound a bit harsh? Sound like maybe Dr. Rosenthal has blown this whole story out of proportion? You might ask, *what does he know, anyway?*

Well, as president of the largest drug treatment program of its kind, Dr. Rosenthal has known thousands of dope smokers — and their problems. So when he spoke, it was more like 15,000 young women and men telling the Senate their stories, too.[h]

New link between personality problems and abnormal brain waves.

A new dimension has recently been added to the study of how pot affects the brain. Dr. Robert Gilkeson, an expert in child and adolescent learning problems, has found that regular pot smoking definitely affects a person's thinking ability. He also says that standard brainwave tests reveal the brain effects of grass.

This psychiatrist has tested over fifty teenagers who have smoked at least three joints a week for four months. Most of these young people were in search of counseling to help them handle their problems. (Many of them hadn't had any psychological problems until they started smoking pot.)

Dr. Gilkeson found abnormal brain waves in all but two of fifty-seven teenagers. He says that grass causes brain waves to be much slower than normal.

Whereas most brain-wave tests require only that the person lie quietly, Dr. Gilkeson asks his subjects to do mental tasks. He says that the sluggish brain waves become obvious when people use their heads during the test. According to Dr. Gilkeson, smokers must lay off dope for several months before their brain waves return to normal.

During the test, he asks patients to do something mentally challenging, like doing math problems in their heads, counting backwards by threes and sevens, or spelling words both forward and backwards. When pot-smokers are forced to think quickly, their brains fail to properly "kick into high gear." Their brain waves can't seem to speed-up when a mental challenge arises.

Dr. Gilkeson has been awarded a grant to complete his study and publish the results. From all indications, this study will point out the following ideas:

1. Surface brain-wave tests can be valuable tools in marijuana research.

2. Regular dopers are less able to "think fast" and do the kind of thinking people need to drive or handle emergencies.

3. As little as two or three joints a week prevent the human brain from working normally.[i]

Studying the heads of overseas "heads."

Dopers of Jamaica, Costa Rica, Greece, Egypt, and India have used grass and hash for many years. Studies of uneducated farmers in Jamaica[25] and Costa Rica[26] found little or no decline in the mental abilities of tokers. However, the problem with these studies is that the farmers, who could barely read, were given written tests — so the results could be about as accurate as a coin toss.

A study of Egyptian hash users told a different story.[27] Over 800 hash heads were compared to 800 nonsmokers. The research team found that more intelligent and better educated users lost far more brain power than poorly educated or less intelligent smokers. In other words, they found *the more you got, the more you lose.*

A study from Greece found a higher level of mental disturbances among grass users.[28] Another study, from India, shows a clear relationship between dope smoking and loss of mental skills. In this study, dopers had lower IQs, poorer memories, slower hand-eye speed, and disturbed time judgment.[29]

Without memory, we soon forget.

Memory is commonly mentioned as a victim of marijuana use. It is well-known that short-term memory decreases while one is "under the influence." This fact doesn't seem to alarm too many folks — if their memories return good as ever when the buzz is gone! What does the research show?

Both the Egyptian and Indian studies found a significant loss of memory power in long-time marijuana and hash smokers. The other studies mentioned did not. However, the studies finding memory losses looked at far more smokers than the other surveys. These human studies are backed up by tests on lab animals that say dope interferes with learning and memory.[10,30] (Remember, the psychiatrists mentioned earlier in this chapter also reported poor memory as a common complaint of their pot-smoking patients.)

On the other hand, there are studies that claim pot is not harmful to the brain. But these studies don't explain away newer research that says dope can probably fog up the old thinking cap.

Surely it will take many more studies before the arguments are all settled. In the meantime, people are still smoking, and millions of memories are on the line.

How about
a Contact High?

Have you ever been to a party where the air was thick with dope smoke? I mean the kind of party where you could splash on a half-bottle of cologne and still come home smelling like the burnt end of a roach clip? If you've ever been to such an affair and didn't turn on, you probably got a "contact high." Whether you actually touched a joint or bong to your lips doesn't alter the fact — you undoubtedly went home with THC in your bloodstream.

What's a contact high? It's a buzz from pot by just being around people who are smoking. All you have to do is breathe.

Until 1977, it was never technically proven. That year, a nonsmoking participant in a marijuana experiment complained of dizziness, red eyes, and a rapid pulse.[1] These symptoms happen to many pot smokers, except the dizziness is called a "high."

The subject was then checked for the THC in his urine. Even though he had not smoked any pot, there was still THC in his system. The amount of pot you can absorb by "contact" is difficult to estimate from this one experiment. (Only a fraction of THC-related chemicals leave the body through the urine. Most pot-products exit via the bowels.)[a] But you can tell from this case that a considerable amount of THC will be absorbed by anyone having sustained, close contact with marijuana smoke.[1,2,3]

This finding is not surprising when you consider how much non-smokers can be bothered by tobacco cigarettes. It's logical. If you inhale smoke, you will absorb the chemicals in it.

So next time you're invited to a pot party, be prepared to breathe the air. If you choose not to have dope-chemicals cruising your arteries, then you have two choices. You could wear a gas mask and filter the smoke. Or, you could spend your time elsewhere.

Dope
and Driving

I'm sure you've heard the unwritten law, "When you drink, don't drive." There is a new one to be added on that list: *"When you smoke pot, drive not."* An impressive heap of evidence shows that stoned drivers are unsafe drivers.

Government reports make the story plain.

In 1976, the Department of Health, Education and Welfare told Congress that marijuana use (at amounts most smokers use) "definitely impairs driving ability." Their report goes on to say that researchers studied "driving-related skills, driver simulator studies, test course performance, actual street driver performance, and most recently, a study of drivers involved in fatal accidents."[1] These studies proved that stoned drivers react slower and make more accident-causing mistakes than straight drivers.

A Massachusetts study found that one in six drivers responsible for fatal accidents was stoned when the accident took place. A California study found that one of seven traffic deaths was caused by stoned drivers.[a] These studies (and many others) prove that driving while stoned causes traffic accidents and deaths.

Don't buy a ticket on Stoned-City Airlines.

Some of the most true-to-life studies done so far are the tests on experienced airplane pilots.[2,3,4] In all of these tests, pilots have always performed far below their undrugged level of skill. In one study, seven professional and three amateur pilots were tested; all had smoked pot for several years. In the test, they either smoked a joint without THC or one with the potency of about one-third a joint. The pilots were tested at different times after smoking.

On the flight simulator, all ten pilots did poorly thirty minutes after toking up. On the average, they made six times as many minor mistakes and seven times as many major ones, compared to when they took the test straight.[b] After two hours they did a little bit better; after four hours they were almost normal. But it took six hours to do as well as they did before smoking.

Poor driving skills outlast the buzz.

The six-hour delay also catches pot-smoking drivers. Some of the effects of pot, like delayed reaction time and poor concentration, seem to last longer than the buzz. Here's what a government report says:

> A continuing danger common to both driving and flying is that some of the perceptual or other performance decrements [decreases] resulting from marijuana use may persist for some time (possibly several hours) beyond the period of subjective intoxication [the buzz]. . . . The individual may attempt to fly or drive without realizing that his or her ability to do so is still impaired although he or she no longer feels high.[1]

So, just like drunk drivers who insist they are ready to drive home, there are still bongers and tokers who swear up and down they can drive just as well stoned. The fact is, dopers need to "come down" for a few hours before they can drive as well as they drive while straight.

Thirty-ton semi trucks can't tell time.

It is known that sense of time is distorted while stoned.[5,6] After smoking, people think time moves slower. Maybe that's why some stoned drivers think they drive better. Things seem to move slower, so drivers believe they have more time to react. But try and tell a speeding, thirty-ton semi that is hogging the center line on a wet road that it's actually moving *real slow,* and that *everything's cool* You won't have time.

Grass and Reproduction

"Grass and Reproduction" is a big category. It includes topics like what pot does to a person's hormones, how it affects the menstrual cycle, and what expectant parents should know about marijuana.

Here are the subjects we'll be looking at in this section:

1. The levels of several key hormones are dropped by pot.
2. Testosterone is immediately affected.
3. A prolonged drop may occur in daily tokers.
4. Women's hormones are also affected.
5. Pot interferes with the powerhouse pituitary.
6. Grass lowers LH in both men and women.
7. Dope can interfere with the menstrual cycle.
8. Sperm counts also can drop.
9. Decreased hormones may mean trouble.
10. Pregnancy and pot is a bad combination.

Key Hormones Dropped by Pot

Everybody has hormones. They're important body chemicals, usually found in very small amounts. Think of them as the "traffic controllers" of the body, ordering everything into its proper place. Males and females have some hormones the same and some different.[a]

Glands such as the pituitary, the adrenals, and the female and male sex glands all produce hormones that are affected by marijuana. Of these glands, pot's action on the adrenals is understood the least. Dope's action on the male hormone, testosterone, is understood the best.

Immediate affects on testosterone.

Testosterone is the hormone most responsible for the male changes of puberty — deepening of voice, growth of beard, increase in muscle mass, and the ability to have children. This chemical continues to play an important role throughout life. It is also essential for the proper development of an unborn male child.[b]

Within hours after a man smokes a joint, his blood level of testosterone takes a nosedive. Carefully run studies show that testosterone levels fall twenty-five to thirty-five percent within three hours after smoking a joint.[1,2] One joint decreases the hormone level about the same as three joints, except that the effect lasts longer with higher doses of pot. Within about twelve hours, the hormones return to their original levels.[c]

A prolonged drop may occur in daily tokers.

Marijuana's long-term effects on the male hormone system are not completely understood. But several detailed studies reveal an interesting pattern.

In a ten-week study, hormone levels were carefully followed in twenty-eight men who smoked five joints a day. As expected, testosterone levels fell after smoking each joint, but they bounced back daily during the first month.

During the fifth week, however, the hormone levels stopped coming all the way back up by the next morning.[2] The levels continued to drop until week nine, when the men stopped smoking. A week without smoking brought the testosterone levels halfway back to their original values. (Another study also showed steady declines in testosterone after subjects smoked daily for four weeks.[3])[d]

So, the male hormone story looks like this: If a man smokes dope, his hormones drop for half a day. If he's a heavy, daily smoker, he needs at least a week (without dope) for his hormones to rise to their original levels.

Because of pot's negative effect on testosterone, THC (pot's main chemical) is considered to be a *demasculinizing*, or *feminizing* agent in men. (In women, however, it does not raise female hormone levels. The "feminizing" effect, then, only occurs in men.) How serious

this effect is, and exactly why it occurs, are still being debated.

Women's hormones are also affected.

The U. S. government forbids the long-term testing of marijuana's effects on women because such tests may harm a woman's child-producing egg cells.[e] Therefore, it is difficult to make clear statements about pot's action on female hormones. But from all indications, women definitely do not get off scott-free from marijuana. THC does not discriminate!

But before we can discuss female hormones, we have to mention the pituitary gland.

Pot interferes with the powerhouse pituitary.

The pituitary is a tiny gland hanging from the underside of the brain. Its powerful hormones control the female and male sex glands as well as the thyroid, the adrenals, and more. It directs how fast and how much we grow. If this little pea dangling within the skull goes whacky, a person can become a giant or a midget.

Scientists do not know if pot can actually harm the pituitary gland. But marijuana definitely interferes with several key pituitary hormones. The main hormones in question are named LH and FSH.[f]

Grass lowers LH in both men and women.

The pituitary hormone, LH, may sound like a very boring subject. But without it, girls and boys would never become women and men. In other words, LH controls puberty. It also controls the female and male reproductive systems in full-grown adults. And when people smoke grass, their LH supplies take a temporary nosedive.

You have already read that testosterone drops when a man takes a toke. LH follows the same pattern, only it drops even more than testosterone. Three hours after getting stoned, a man has lost over a third of his LH (thirty-five percent to forty-five percent).[1] He doesn't regain his original amount of LH until about twelve hours after smoking.

It looks like the same story for women who use dope. Since the government restricts marijuana research on women, much of what we know comes from experiments with Rhesus monkeys.

With one to two joints, the LH of female monkeys is more than cut in half.[4] The LH drops about the same amount when ten joints' worth of THC is given. With large doses of THC, however, the hormones stay down much longer.[g,h]

Dope can interfere with the menstrual cycle.

Many hormones are important in regulating a woman's period. LH plays a key role at the midpoint of the cycle. FSH is also important; like LH, FSH levels decreases when dope is in the body.

In monkeys, THC interferes with certain parts of the menstrual cycle. A blockage of the ovum (egg)-releasing mechanism frequently occurs as a result of marijuana's chemicals.[4,i]

Increases in irregular periods have also been reported among women who smoke grass.[j]

Sperm counts also can drop.

As you probably know, the father's sperm cell unites with the mother's egg cell to make a baby. Each month, a woman releases one egg to be fertilized. However, a man produces many millions of sperm cells each day. Many sperm cells are usually needed for a man to father a child. In fact, some men with millions of sperm cells still do not have enough to have children.

The reasons why a man needs many sperm to make one baby are complicated. Doctors test for whether a man has enough sperm by doing a *sperm count*. It is important to mention sperm counts because grass has been shown to cause the number of sperm to decrease.

In one study, five male volunteers smoked over ten joints a day for four weeks. This is a lot of dope, and their sperm counts plummeted as a result. On the average, the number of sperm each man produced (after four weeks of heavy burning) was less than half of what it was at the start of the experiment.[5,k]

In other words, heavy pot smoking tends to decrease sperm counts quite a bit. How this effect alters a man's ability to have children, and what occasional pot use does to sperm are not well understood.

The importance of decreased hormones.

There is no doubt that pot causes a temporary decrease of several key hormones. But is that fact anything to get all bent out of shape about? Are we talking about a real health danger-or just a harmless change in body chemistry? Guess what — scientists aren't sure.

However, this fact may be very important for one large group of people — young men and women going through puberty. During the teen years, the body changes into adulthood. These changes largely depend on the hormones just mentioned. The amounts of these hormones increase greatly during the rapid growth years of junior high and high school.

When a single joint knocks down testosterone and the pituitary hormones for several hours, regular smoking during the teen years could conceivably mess something up permanently. Even though these hormones come back up within a day, daily smokers will continuously have a lower supply of these important body chemicals. Exactly what effect constantly lowered hormones has on puberty and on the adult reproductive system is not known.[1]

It stands to reason that the young women and men with the most to lose are those in whom puberty is delayed or those whose hormone levels are slightly low to begin with. At the very least, decreased hormones is a sure sign that something's out of proper balance.

Pregnancy and Pot — A Bad Combination

As if all this hormone stuff weren't enough to think about, women who are pregnant also face the possibility of damaging their unborn children. We've talked about many good reasons for not smoking pot — but pregnancy is easily the best reason to not do dope.

If mommy tokes, junior also gets stoned.

From studies on animals, we know that THC goes straight from the mother to her unborn baby.[6,7] The child is partially protected by the *placenta*. This "factory," a special organ of pregnancy, stops over half of the THC before it reaches the baby's blood. But at this stage of life, even a little THC is far too much.

Remember, THC interferes with normal building activities in cells. Less *protein* is formed, as well as less *DNA* and *RNA*. These are all vital ingredients for growing new cells. And nobody grows new cells faster than a child in the womb. Therefore, it is obvious that THC could cause *nothing but trouble* for a developing baby.

Mothers who breast feed their children must consider another dope-related fact. THC *definitely* goes into the breast milk.[8,9] Even though mother's milk is the best possible food for an infant, milk loaded with dope is quite another story.

Dope harms the child-bearing process in lab animals.

Most of the information about pot and pregnancy comes from studies on laboratory animals. It would be unthinkable to test pregnant women with large doses of THC. Instead, thousands of rats, mice, and rabbits have given us these results.

Several problems are commonly seen in pregnant animals given THC. Their litters contain fewer young and the offspring weigh less than normal. More young are born dead and more are lost (aborted) before birth.[10,11] When very large amounts of THC are given, there is an increase in birth defects, especially defects of the brain and nervous system.[12,13] In one study, the offspring of THC-treated rats had smaller brains than undrugged rats.[14]

It also appears that THC affects the cells of younger animals more than the cells of older ones. THC decreases production of brain proteins more severely in infant rats than in rats of any other age.[8,m] Brain tissue, which has a high fat content, attracts the THC molecule.[15] Since THC slows cell growth, the possibility of harmful brain effects in a developing human cannot be ruled out.

Baby boys have an extra worry.

The following facts could add up to an *extra* worry for male children of mothers who toke:

1. A male child needs testosterone before birth to develop normal sexual function as an adult.

2. THC decreases testosterone levels in males. THC is also transferred from a mother to her unborn or nursing children.

3. Experimental evidence in mice suggests that the adult sexual function of males is threatened by mothers who toke during pregnancy.

Dr. Susan Dalterio tested whether THC given to mothers could damage the adult sexual function of their male offspring. Each day, pregnant and nursing mothers were given three joints worth of THC. In this way, the babies only received THC from their mothers' bloodstreams (before birth) and through the breast milk (after birth).

The male offspring had no visible defects at birth. However, when the sons of THC-treated mothers reached adulthood, they were physically inferior to untreated mice. The THC mice had smaller testes and were flabby and obese. In addition, the THC mice were less sexually active than normal adult male mice.[16,n]

What does this research mean for humans? It's hard to say, partly because sexual development in humans is far more complex than in mice. But humans (like mice) also have a "critical period" when unborn male children produce high levels of testosterone. And marijuana smoked during pregnancy definitely gets into the child's bloodstream. When you add all that to the way THC lowers testosterone in males, you come up with another dope-related health risk — especially for the Jimmys, Joeys, and Johnnys of the world.

Monkeys say, "Mothers beware."

A five-year study on Rhesus monkeys brings the parenthood part of the dope story even closer to home. For five years, nineteen female monkeys were fed THC that was baked into raisin cookies. The amount of dope given was equal to one or two joints a day for a person. Since over a million American women smoke that much pot, this major study may have serious implications for women of childbearing age. It's worth repeating that eating pot has less effect than smoking it (the lungs absorb more THC than the gut).

During the five years of the experiment, females given THC lost about four times as many babies as the untreated females.[17] The monkeys eating "loaded" cookies lost four of every ten pregnancies, (from babies born dead, miscarried, or dead soon after birth). Of undrugged mothers, the babies were lost in only one of ten pregnancies.

The surviving female offspring of drugged and undrugged mothers alike were of normal size. However, male infants of THC-treated mothers were clearly smaller than male monkeys born to undrugged mothers. The "THC infants" were also described as far more *hyperactive* and irritable than their undrugged "cousins."[o] In humans, some cases of hyperactivity are thought to be caused by problems in the brain or nervous system.

A painful lesson from mothers who drink.

The example of alcohol use during pregnancy is a good warning sign for marijuana smokers. It was recently discovered that children of mothers who drank a lot while pregnant have far more serious health problems than children born to nondrinking mothers.[18] These serious problems include birth defects and withdrawal symptoms.[p]

Scientists now believe that a woman who smokes cigarettes while pregnant also threatens her unborn child.

THC's powerful negative effects on cell growth are well known. With this in mind, plus the painful lessons of alcohol and tobacco use, need we see a whole generation of marijuana babies before we know pregnancy and pot don't mix?

In this chapter we have touched upon marijuana's unwanted effects on hormones, sperm counts, and menstrual cycles. We also mentioned research that says grass is a serious risk for women considering motherhood.

There is still much to be learned about marijuana and the birth process. In the meantime, while doctors sift through the clues, why play "Russian Roulette" with the family tree?

Grass, Genes, and Chromosomes

For over a decade, scientists have studied whether pot causes chromosome damage. Early studies claimed that marijuana users had more abnormal cells than non users.[1,2] Other doctors disagreed and said grass caused no such damage.[3,4]

Why the Hassle over Genes and Chromosomes?

Genes and *chromosomes* are the blueprint for making new cells. Found in the heart of each cell, they contain the instructions that cells follow when they divide and grow. Every normal human cell has forty-six chromosomes. *Genes* are the areas along each crisscross-shaped chromosome.[a] A chemical that disturbs this *genetic* blueprint can cause two major problems — cancer and birth defects. In the case of marijuana, the issue is not settled. Still, there are hints that tokers run a greater risk of messing up this delicate genetic system.

Chromosomes may break.

If a piece of a chromosome breaks off, that's called a *chromosome break*. The result is obvious — something gets left out when new cells are formed.

Some people have argued that pot causes chromosome breaks.[1,2,5] Just as many scientists (if not more) claim this damage does not happen.[3,4,6]

Lost chromosomes and marijuana.

Several studies point to a different kind of chromosome problem from grass — lost chromosomes. Cells with less than the normal forty-six chromosomes don't know what to do when it's time to divide. These cells are in just as much trouble as cells with broken chromosomes.

One research team found that pot smokers had far more blood cells with missing chromosomes than non-tokers. They looked at over 60,000 white blood cells from non-smokers and from people who smoked over three joints a week for two years. The tokers had over twice as many cells with missing chromosomes.[7] The scientists then took blood cells from non-smokers and added THC to the cells. The cells became abnormal in the same way — lost chromosomes.[b]

A more recent study showed that volunteers had far more blood cells with missing chromosomes than normal during a four-week period of smoking fourteen joints a day. Ten days off dope brought the number of abnormal cells down somewhat, but there were still more missing chromosomes than when the test started.[8]

Swiss researchers have found this same result in human lung cells. In these experiments, which were also described in the section on lungs, healthy lung cells were given daily puffs of marijuana smoke for two months. These cells had reduced numbers of chromosomes far more often than cells not exposed to marijuana.[9]

Cancer, anyone?

When cells start to grow wild in the body, it is called *cancer*. When the Swiss researchers just mentioned continued the smoke treatment longer than two months, the cells began to look more and more like cancer cells. These lung cells went wild in their test dishes.[9,c] It's a good hint that dope can cause cancer in the lungs, too.

One scientist injected THC into the shoulders of 200 mice. These weekly THC shots caused cancer of the muscle in four of the mice. Four of 200 may not sound like much, but mice almost *never* get muscle cancer.[10] None of the mice that got fake shots (with no THC) got cancer.[d]

In the chapter on lungs, we mentioned studies that show cancer is more likely in dope users. The next chapter (on immunity) will also examine how the body's cancer-stopping defenses might be weakened by grass.

Bogus blood cells found in Greek hash heads.

One study looked at blood cells from male Greek hashish smokers. On the average, these men had smoked hash for twenty-five years.

Under a microscope, white blood cells of these men were clearly abnormal. Almost two-thirds of the smokers had cells with a *drumstick nucleus*.[11] Big deal, huh?

A drumstick nucleus is normally found in the cells of all women. (That's how male impostors competing as female athletes can be found out.) But only one out of 500 men have cells with a drumstick nucleus.[12]

In this study, twenty-one of thirty-four men had blood cells with this "female" marker. Exactly what this finding means for your run-of-the-mill toker is not well understood. Finding drumsticks in over sixty percent of male hashish users, however, surely indicates something is a bit

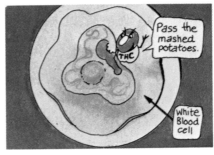

haywire.[e] In case you are wondering, this picture is a microsopic view of a drumstick nucleus with a THC molecule "on board."

Eggs and Sperm — Important Cells Threatened by THC

As most folks know, the female egg cell and the male sperm cell join to make a baby. Marijuana is known to damage both eggs and sperm; the big question is how serious the changes are.

Men produce millions of sperm cells each day. So any damage to these cells might be reversed as soon as smoking is stopped. (Scientists aren't sure.) But the story is far different for women.

Once you break an egg, it can't be fixed.

A female is born with less than a half-million egg cells, and she never makes another. Starting at puberty, one egg is released each month. If a damaged egg cell is released and fertilized, a damaged baby can result. The fact that women don't make new egg cells is the reason that pot tests on women are severely restricted by the U. S. government.

One scientist tested how the egg cells of mice were affected when moderate doses of THC were given. One hundred fifty young adult female mice were given THC and then were mated. When the fertilized eggs had just begun to divide, the eggs were examined.

About half of the eggs from the mice given THC were either dead or severely damaged. About a quarter of the living eggs were damaged. Almost all the eggs of the mice *not* given THC were normal.[f]

There have not been many studies on what THC does to egg cells. But it is obvious that any damage to the egg cells cannot be undone.

Sperm cells are very sensitive to chemicals.

In men, new sperm cells are constantly being made to take the place of older cells. Researchers have shown that sperm cells are quite sensitive to marijuana's effects.

In a recent Canadian study, mice given THC showed abnormal sperm cells.[13] For five days, the mice had been given THC equal to several joints a day. The THC mice showed two to four times as many abnormal sperm as the untreated mice. (Whereas a normal mouse sperm has a hook on the end, an abnormal mouse sperm is often missing the hook or shaped too thin.) In this experiment, several other chemicals found in grass (besides THC) also caused abnormal sperm.[8]

In the study of Greek hash heads (where "drumsticks" were found), the researchers viewed the men's sperm under a high-powered electron microscope. They found definite abnormalities in the sperm. With special methods, the sperm was checked for protein — and the sperm cells came up short. Instead of being almost solid protein, like normal sperm, the hash users' sperm looked spotty, practially moth-eaten.[11]

In another study of five smokers who used at least three joints per week, marijuana definitely had a negative effect on sperm. After two weeks off drugs, the men worked up to eight or more joints a day. (One man smoked thirty-one doobies in one day.) After smoking for a month, they went cold turkey for two weeks.

By the end of the final two weeks, all five subjects had a reduced sperm count. A *sperm count* is the number of sperm cells in a sample. On the average, the sperm counts were less than half of their starting point values.[14] In addition, the sperm cells were sluggish in their movements, compared to before the test.

What's it all mean?

As always, the important question is what do these findings mean for human pot-smokers? This will be a more difficult question than whether pot harms the lungs or brain. The lungs and brain can be tested with more and more advanced tests. But proof for damaged genes and chromosomes shows up in *future generations* of children.

This kind of proof is very difficult, maybe impossible, to obtain. Some *mutations* (the results of damaged chromosomes) don't show up for several generations. Some only appear as a weakness somewhere in the body. Only time will unfold this chapter of the marijuana story.

This book has used a lot of cliches, lots of common expressions. Here goes another one: Where your chromosomes are concerned, an ounce of prevention is worth a pound of cure.

Marijuana and Immunity

Marijuana probably weakens body defenses against disease. It hinders the growth and action of cells that fight germs. However, whether dopers actually get more diseases than non-dopers isn't settled yet.

Pot acts on the body's cold and flu defenses.

Your body has two main ways to fight disease. The defense team that pot burdens the most is the *cell-mediated* system. This system guards against colds and flu (viruses), protects from cancer and funguses, and is involved in certain skin reactions.[a]

Doctors who study human tokers disagree.

Most scientists who study the immune (defense) system believe regular dope smokers have (at the least) slightly weakened defenses. However, experiments on actual pot users have given different results.

Part of the disagreements involve which tests are run. For instance, when doctors measure how well their patients' anti-virus cells respond to foreign red blood cells, pot users usually have weaker defenses.[1,2,b]

Skin tests of dopers show little or no weakness in their bodies.[3] However, a skin test is not as accurate as a foreign red blood cell test. So a negative skin test means that the tested pot smoker isn't an immune cripple, but it doesn't prove she or he has no weakness in body defenses.[c] Other tests on dopers vary; some show dope does cause a person to have less disease protection,[4,5] some show dope doesn't.[6,7]

Stoned rats and mice are less defense-minded.

There is little doubt that laboratory animals given THC have less active body defenses.[8,9,10] (Effective defense cells must move, grow, and divide very quickly when germs arrive.) The defense cells of rats and mice that get high a lot grow and divide slower when challenged by an invading foreign cell or chemical. Guard cells also move slower in a doped-up rodent.

Mice given THC show another defense problem. They have a lowered ability to reject foreign *skin grafts,* pieces of skin from another mouse.[11,d] The skin graft test is a way to show the strength of the immunity system. If the mouse keeps the graft, his system is weak. If his body resists the graft, his system is strong.

Normally, the body destroys all cells (including germs) that are not its own. That's why kidney transplant patients need special drugs to prevent the new kidney from being rejected.[e] A good defense system also destroys cancer cells before they can gain any headway. Therefore, any weakening of body defenses would make cancer more likely.

Defense cells + THC = weak cells.

As you already know, THC interferes with the growth and activity of all cells. Immunity cells are no exception. As we discussed earlier, when defense cells from humans or animals are given THC, they grow slower, move slower and respond poorly to invaders.[12,13]

Many of the body's defense cells move around in the blood. When THC gets into the blood and begins to do its thing, it is only logical that defense cells become slower.

Dope weakens the first line of defense.

Most disease germs are breathed in through the lungs. The lungs have cells called *macrophages*. These cells eat germs and they have the first shot at stopping a disease before it settles in. When your macrophages are stoned out on grass, "bugs" can slide by without much trouble.

When you smoke a joint, it takes several hours before your macrophages can work again at full strength to fight disease.[14] Cigarette smoke also reduces the germ-killing ability of macrophages, but dope smoke slows these cells down far more than tobacco smoke.[f]

As you can tell, there are lots of clues that say pot makes it harder to stay healthy. Still, scientists aren't sure whether tokers get more colds, flu, and cancer than non-tokers. (You can imagine that a study to prove that hunch would take thousands of people and millions of dollars.)

In the meantime, it is obvious that pot can do some type of harm to cells involved in body defense. How much of this effect pot has on the average user is still unknown. Pot smokers are surely not defenseless, by any means. On the other hand, there is reason to suspect at least some decrease in disease-preventing ability.

Can You Get Hooked?

Guess what? The most up-to-date information shows that grass fills many of the requirements to be called an addicting drug. No doubt many of you think that's nonsense — especially you pot smokers. I am sure you have heard, for many years, that marijuana is definitely not addicting. Well, the best evidence now seems to suggest otherwise.

In this section, we're going to go over what these terms mean, and how they apply to marijuana:

1. *Tolerance* is when the body needs increasing amounts of grass to get high.
2. *Drug-seeking behavior* shows a person's dependence on drugs.
3. *Withdrawal symptoms* occur when a person gets sick because a habit-forming drug is suddenly cut off.
4. *Addiction* is when it's hard to quit.

Tolerance definitely occurs with grass.

Tolerance means you need more and more of a drug to get the same result. It's like someone who has been a drinker all his life. He needs more booze than a non-drinker to get drunk. Of course, many people would rather say they *can handle more,* instead of they *need more* to get high. It still means the same thing.

When scientists talk about "tolerance" to a drug, they are describing something physical. The mind has little or nothing to do with it. When the body learns to burn up the drug faster and faster, more and more of the drug is needed (This is usually how tolerance works.)[a]

It is a well-known fact that grass users can show tolerance to the drug's physical effects. In 1976, the Department of Health, Education and Welfare told Congress: "Carefully conducted studies with known doses of marijuana or THC leave little question that tolerance develops with prolonged use."[1]

That regular smokers need more and more pot or hashish to get high was first discovered by studying people in different countries. Hashish users in Europe and Asia could take enough THC to knock out the Lone Ranger's horse. Some of these people could easily handle over fifty potent reefers per day.[2]

In the last ten years, experiments have shown tolerance to occur under many different conditions. This effect has been proven with rats taught to press bars and climb ropes[3], with the incidence of fighting activity among Siamese fighting-fish[4], with pigeons pecking at a disc to get food[5], and with baby chicks taught to avoid a hot-plate[6], just to name a few. Thus, tolerance to marijuana definitely checks out at the zoo.

Tolerance has also been proven in humans. Scientists can use the EEG machine to tell if a person is buzzed or straight. The machine shows a person's brain waves, and when the brain waves look a certain way you can tell the person is stoned.

In one study, scientists used the EEG on two groups of people. One group only used pot several times a week. The other group had used hash for over twenty years. Compared to the occasional users, the experienced smokers required four to ten times the amount of dope to make their brain waves look stoned.[7] This study shows long-term users' tolerance to the effects of pot; their bodies need far greater doses to get high.

In another study, scientists showed that people can become tolerant to THC (pot's main chemical). For this test they chose people who had smoked grass for four years.

The test lasted a month. For the first week, no one was allowed to smoke any dope. Each day of the second and third weeks, everybody took ten joints' worth of THC. The last week, nobody was given any THC.

What happened? Well, the first few days they felt really stoned from the dope. But they got less and less stoned everyday, even though they were using the same amount of THC.[8] Some people even threatened to quit the experiment because they weren't getting high enough. But these same people, who were hardly getting stoned, got physically sick when they had to stop the THC.[6] (We will mention this when we talk about withdrawal symptoms.)

Tolerance developed so strongly and so quickly in this experiment because the drug was given throughout the day. When THC floods the brain morning, noon, and night, it quickly becomes "old stuff" and greater amounts are needed to get high. Other experiments, lasting twenty-one[9] and ninety-four days[10] show the same thing.[c]

Physical tolerance is most likely to develop in a person who uses dope for months or years. It is more common when people smoke several joints a day, or in people who use strong forms of grass, like hash. In addition, a period of laying off seems to reverse most of the tolerance effect.[11]

Over ten years ago a study claimed that experienced users actually need *less* dope than beginners.[12] This was called "reverse tolerance," and it has been shown to be a *myth*. In that particular study, the scientists didn't check out how strong the THC in the dope was. All other studies since then show that the dose of marijuana needed to affect a person never decreases with regular use.

Drug-Seeking Behavior

Tolerance alone does not prove marijuana is addicting. There is a lot more involved to getting hooked. In fact, doctors don't all agree about what, exactly, an addicting drug is.

Most scientists agree that a person addicted to drugs shows tolerance. But take cigarette smokers. They don't need higher and higher doses; a one-pack-a-day habit usually stays at one pack. So are cigarettes addicting, even though smokers don't show tolerance? You bet your shoelaces they are!

Anyone who has ever tried to quit cigarettes can tell you that tobacco is habit-forming. No doubt about it, "coffin nails," as they are called, "hook" the user. Cigarette puffers have been known to do strange things at all hours of the night to find a smoke. This is called *drug-seeking be-*  *havior,* and it often goes along with dependence to a drug.

Do pot-smokers demonstrate this drug-seeking behavior? That has not been proven. It would be quite difficult to actually show this behavior in a laboratory. Instead, observe yourself, or pot-smoking friends, after the next bag runs out. Do you (or they) get itchy to find more? Are people willing to break other plans in order to score a bag? If so, you have just seen drug-seeking behavior in action.

Withdrawal — The Cold Turkey Way to Quit

The thing most people think of when talking about drug dependence is *withdrawal*. Withdrawal means to just quit, to go cold turkey. When a drug-user quits suddenly, without tapering-off, there is a period of "hurtin' for certain". You often see chills, jitters, cramps, nausea, vomiting, and cold sweats. A person in withdrawal may show just a few of these symptoms, or many of them. Withdrawal continues until the body gets used to not having the drug in the blood.

Withdrawal often happens when users of hard narcotics, alcohol, downers, and cigarettes go cold turkey. Withdrawal from some drugs is worse than from others. Also, some people will get sicker than others.

Does this occur with marijuana smokers? Some experts say yes, some say no. Before we talk about studies, let's look in on some folks who have just run out of grass.

Perhaps this scene is not so far-fetched. Remember the month-long test you read about already? Those people got sick when they couldn't get any dope in the last week of the experiment. Their withdrawal symptoms included sweating, hot flashes, irritability, insomnia, hiccups, increased salivation, weight loss, and brain-wave changes.[8] They were sick for three to four days.[d] Other doctors have reported withdrawal symptoms in long-time, heavy users who suddenly quit.[13,14] One researcher showed the same thing with THC-treated monkeys.[15]

THC and morphine: Chemical cousins.

Scientists have found an interesting connection between hard narcotics (like heroin, morphine, and opium) and THC: Narcotics and THC are both counteracted by a drug used to treat overdose victims.

Naloxone instantly stops the chemical effects of narcotics. Overdose victims in a coma (near death) sometimes wake up and head for the door as soon as naloxone is given. Even though it can save lives in narcotics overdoses, naloxone has little or no effect on most other drugs. (For example, a person who OD's from "ludes" or "reds" will not be helped by naloxone.) *But naloxone does stop the action of THC.*

When scientists give high daily doses of THC to rats, and then give the rats naloxone, the rats go into withdrawal (diarrhea, teeth-chattering, "wet-dog" shakes, weight loss).[16,17] Withdrawal signs will also occur if naloxone is given to heroin or morphine addicts.[e] This anti-narcotic has not yet been tested on human pot users. From these experiments, though, it is clear that THC is a chemical cousin of morphine, opium, and other hard narcotics.

Delayed THC release may disguise marijuana withdrawal.

THC stays in the body a long time. It is stored in places in the body that are high in fat and it's constantly taken out of storage as well. Small amounts of THC can be found in the blood for several weeks after smoking a joint. That may be why most pot smokers don't have painful withdrawal symptoms, like alcoholics or heroin addicts do.

Even when dope smokers cut off the drug, THC is still present in the body.[f]

Addiction — The Argument Still Rages

Some researchers have found no evidence of a marijuana withdrawal syndrome. Others have reported "maybe" withdrawal symptoms, like irritability, weight loss, and sleeplessness. Among scientists, the argument still rages about whether marijuana should be officially called an addicting drug.

Some people claim you can get hooked on grass, but only mentally hooked. They say you only think you need it, but your body doesn't really need it. From the evidence mentioned in this chapter, though, it looks like a craving for marijuana also has a physical explanation.

Addiction —·The Bottom Line

The bottom line to all the arguments is this: How hard is it to actually stop smoking marijuana once you really decide to quit? This question tells the real story of dependence on any habit.

People have many habits. Some are easier to quit than others, so not all habits are addictions. Consider the following examples and decide about grass for yourself.

Some people go bananas if they can't find a cola to drink. Not only that, they often have to have a certain brand. Quite clearly, you can get hooked on colas. They contain large amounts of caffeine (a drug classified as a stimulant, like speed).[g] Soft drinks also contain a lengthy list of other bizarre chemicals.[h]

You see lots of ads that describe how soft drinks will make your life more exciting. These companies lay out a dream world where everything is rosier if you chug their drink. These come-ons are obviously straight-out cons, cleverly designed to suck people into expensive and unhealthy habits. But when people see these ridiculous ads often enough, they can start to believe them. The same is true for ads that sell booze or cigarettes. These companies claim they are selling good times that the people want (and millions of buyers agree). Like it or not, they are also selling health hazards and addictions. You can't buy the fun without the trouble; it's a package deal.[i,j]

Coffee and tea also contain caffeine. Many folks get the blues if their coffee supply is shut down. You can say the same thing about people who crave sugar.

Some people don't agree, but I think millions are hooked on sweet stuff. I'm not talking about sugar found in grains, fruits, and vegetables. I'm referring to the massive quantities of refined sugar added to candies, cream-filled pastries, soft drinks, and many breakfast cereals.[k]

When a person constantly shovels down sweets, the delicate sugar-balancing machinery gets revved-up to handle these heavy loads of sugar. The person's body gets used to it — hooked, you might say. Many people get quite upset if they can't get their "sugar fix." They will often display  obvious drug-seeking behavior, dropping everything to go hunt down a bag of jelly donuts.

What folks eat and drink is entirely their own business. I am just pointing out a few examples of things most people don't consider addicting. Plain and simple, though, once these "foods" become habits, they are plenty tough to quit.

Whether an addiction is mental or physical, is really not important. *Difficulty in quitting tells the full story of addiction for any habit;* marijuana is no exception.

If you ask around, you can probably learn more about whether pot is addicting than you will learn from any book. Talk to people who have quit dope or have tried to give it up. A lot of them will tell you quitting pot is no piece of cake.

Scientists will need at least a few years to agree about marijuana's ability to "hook" a user. In the meantime, the clues you get with your own eyes and ears might be the best proof you will find.

In Search of the Perfect Study

Some of you might ask, "Why don't they just do one big study on all of this stuff, instead of fooling around with mice and rats?" What most of us want to know is *"How harmful is marijuana for people?"* Except for scientists, most folks don't really care what a load of THC does to some poor mouse. They want it translated into human beings. Fair enough, but easier said than done.

We have already touched on reasons why doctors still don't have enough answers about grass. This chapter will put the basic problems facing marijuana researchers into simple terms. It will show why *both* of the following statements can be made without telling a lie: The long-term effects of marijuana are *not yet known*. The long-term use of marijuana is *clearly hazardous* to a person's health.

We will also examine a famous study that proves you can't believe everything you read.

People can't always be tested.

Obviously, some tests just cannot be run on people. For example, you already have read about a study where rats were forced to smoke marijuana for a year. One year of dope smoking caused the rats' lungs to become diseased, perhaps permanently.[1] Would we now want to test humans to see how much dope their lungs could take before they were permanently damaged? Of course not! But since a rat lung is not a human lung, this experiment still leaves scientists without positive proof on human beings, right? Very true.

No sane doctor would ever design a test that would cause permanent damage to a person. Such a doctor would have his conscience to deal with. He would also have to confront the people who became ill; that scientist would probably get sued for ten zillion dollars.

It is also impossible to test pot's effect on a developing baby. Feeding dope to pregnant women is obviously out of the question.

As you can see, we can't always get straight answers about grass by testing people. You still hear "The long-term effects of marijuana are not yet known" because proving the human effects *beyond a shadow of a doubt* is almost impossible. Still, scientists know quite a bit about pot's long-term effects. Much of their information comes from studying animals.

Animals offer key benefits.

Laboratory animals can be tested so that scientists can tell exactly what causes what. They know exactly what the animals eat and how much they sleep. (Also, mice are very small, so they fit in the cages better than people!)

Rats and mice only live a couple of years, so a year of dope for them equals several years for a person. Therefore, you could test a mouse that gets stoned all through puberty in a short period of time. But would *you* like to be locked up in a research ward through your entire teen years?

In addition, laboratory animals can be sacrificed for science and their tissues can be looked at under a microscope. Over the years, many human lives have been saved because of tests run on rats and mice.

Rats are super dopers.

Ounce for ounce, rats, mice and other small critters can safely handle far greater drug dosages than humans. It usually takes several rat-sized joints just to get a rat stoned!

In doing marijuana research, doctors must consider this complicated fact: Rats and mice are *super dopers*. Rodent bodies are constantly in high gear. For example, a rat's heart beats over twice as fast as a person's. Now you can see why they burn up drugs much faster than people.

Some people have criticized the high doses of THC given to rats and mice, *without* taking into account that rodents are super dopers. In many experiments, these critters get THC doses equal to twenty joints a day (or more). People have glanced at these figures and said, "That's so much dope, this experiment ain't worth a nickle." But when you consider that mice burn up drugs over ten times as fast as humans, twenty joints a day is actually more like two joints a day. When you consider the rapid body chemistry of rats and mice, these doses of THC begin to look more reasonable.

By taking into account all the facts about how rats and mice handle dope, we can get some valuable answers from our little fuzzy friends.[a]

People can still be studied.

Even with all the problems of testing, scientists can still examine human tokers. There are two ways to study the effects of grass on people. First, a scientist can put volunteers in a hospital ward for so many weeks, give them marijuana and run lots of tests. Just like the studies of caged mice, the scientist knows exactly how much dope the volunteers get and when they get it.

However, such a test can only tell us about the short-term effects of grass. By this method, scientists have learned about pot's effects on memory, hormones, and driving skills.

When the tests run for weeks, doctors can often use very sensitive equipment to get clues about pot's long-term effects. In this way, they have gathered important facts about how tolerance to pot occurs, as well as what grass does to the lungs, hormones, sperm counts, and cell structure.

You can probably guess what the drawbacks to these studies are. One, they're too brief to reveal all the effects of years of pot smoking. Two, the tests must be stopped before the test volunteers become permanently damaged. Three, these studies are very expensive!

Just figure the average cost of a hospital bed per day, times a couple of months, times a few dozen subjects? Realistically, a shortage of research funds is a big reason these studies can't be long enough to tell us all they could.

Scientists can also be on the lookout for heavy burners.

The other way of studying marijuana's human effects is to find people who have been smoking pot (by their own choice) for a long time. The researcher then examines them medically to look for such telltale signs as lung trouble, blood cell changes, and memory losses.

These studies are called *surveys,* and they are loaded with problems. For example, the scientist can never be sure what the people looked like before they started smoking grass. If he does find something, how does he know dope caused it when he couldn't check his subjects out  beforehand? He can't be sure exactly how much pot they used. A person might tell him, "Oh yea, man, far-out, like I usually do a couple of bongs at lunch, and I'm really heavy into brownies, and then I share a doobie with my friends every chance I get." How does the scientist convert that to milligrams of THC?[b]

Researchers can't be sure how long the subjects used grass, and the pot used may vary in strength. It might have had chemicals like PCP or paraquat added to it. Also it's hard to tell how many other drugs the subjects have used. To be reasonably accurate, survey-type studies must include more people than a well-designed laboratory experiment.

Building the story piece by piece.

As you can tell, scientists studying marijuana get information from many places. They use facts from animal studies and studies on human tokers. They look at tissue culture and microscope slides. All in all, scientists try and put the big picture together, piece by piece, from everything they know.

And they can get definite answers! Consider for a moment a jury trial. In some cases, even if there are no witnesses to a crime, the jury still can figure out who's guilty because of the clues (a gun with fingerprints, for instance.) Well, scientists do the same thing as a jury. They see the clues and then they figure out "who did it."

In a summary of current pot research, one scientist answers the question, "Does pot cause damage to the body?" He answers, "Damage beyond a doubt."[c] This leading British scientist was talking about the overwhelming evidence that pot can damage the reproductive process.[2] He also believes that without a doubt, pot damages the lungs and immune system. In his book, *Marijuana: Biological Effects,* he shows that even without clear *human* evidence, the jury has brought in a guilty verdict on marijuana.

As it stands, many leading scientists believe we already know plenty about pot's health effects. Most doctors actively involved in marijuana research feel grass is clearly harmful to health. The big question is *how harmful.*

Other scientists prefer just to say, "We don't have all the answers yet." (Some folks mistake that to mean there aren't any harmful effects.) Unfortunately, all the facts won't be in for many years.

But people want answers about marijuana *today.* They want to know what scientists *do* know about grass. They want to be filled in as new discoveries are made. They *don't* want to wait twenty years for the final word.

From the scientists' end of it, the search for the perfect study continues.

The "Jamaica Study" — A Victim of Progress

Of all marijuana research projects, the "Jamaica study" is the most famous. Without question, it has shaped more opinions about marijuana's safety than any other single work. So it deserves a closer look.

The Jamaica study shows that you can't believe everything you read. In the interest of setting the record straight, we will now examine this study closely.

"Ganja in Jamaica" is the proper name of the study.[3] A strong variety of marijuana — called *ganja* — grows wild in Jamaica. Because some native Jamaicans smoke ganja practically all their lives, a group of researchers thought Jamaica was a good place to study the health effects of years of marijuana use.

Although the study was finished in 1972, it looks newer because the publishing date on the report is listed as 1975.

In this survey, thirty Jamaican field workers who smoked ganja were compared to thirty who did not. Medical tests were designed to look for lung, brain, and chromosome damage. The authors of the report found little or no difference between the smokers and non-smokers. They concluded that "Chronic [long-term] use of potent cannabis [pot] is not toxic to the human mind and body."[3]

The conclusions of the report were highly publicized by the media. Many people still consider the study to be proof that marijuana presents little or no risk to the user.

On the contrary, the report is filled with major weaknesses. No doubt the authors designed the best study they could in 1970. Still, a brief examination of the facts shows the conclusions of "Ganja in Jamaica" to be completely inaccurate. There is simply no way the medical data can back up the statement that marijuana is completely harmless. Here's why.

Not enough people were studied.

The study tested only thirty smokers, quite a small group. To compare, a study of thirty life-long cigarette smokers could easily miss the well-known link that cigarettes cause lung cancer, emphysema, and heart disease. You need to look at more people to find out anything.

In all fairness to the researchers, they didn't have enough money to study a larger group of smokers. The point is, with only thirty subjects, the researchers still took the plunge and said that smoking strong grass for years wasn't the least bit harmful. That story grabbed a lot of headlines in American newspapers.

The great smoke-off: Ganja versus tobacco.

The report said that smoking pot doesn't hurt the lungs. The researchers said they couldn't find much difference between the lungs of the dopers and non-dopers. But of the thirty so-called "nonsmokers" in the study, about two-thirds smoked cigarettes. To say they don't smoke, even though they smoke tobacco, is so ridiculous it's almost funny. In a study on lung damage, cigarette smokers just do not belong in the nonsmoker group.

If you look *closely* at the study's evidence, it *still* looks like the ganja smokers had worse lungs. For example, the smokers had lower levels of oxygen in their blood, a possible sign that their lungs weren't properly moving air into the blood. In addition, they had higher red cell counts than normal. This finding shows their bodies possibly weren't getting enough oxygen.[d]

Some breathing tests were also given. But tests now known to be more valuable in finding lung problems were not done. The few tests the researchers did run still had the ganja smokers coming out on the short end of the "lung stick." The differences were not dramatic, but they were there.

X-rays were used to look for lung damage. The x-rays didn't find much in either group. However, we now know that x-rays aren't very valuable in studying pot smokers; other methods tell us much more about what grass does to the lungs.[e]

This study *does not* prove grass doesn't harm the lungs. Remember, the ganja users were compared to a group made up of mostly cigarette smokers. Having worse lungs than cigarette lungs is a pretty tough act to follow.

The chromosome syndrome — if you can't grow 'em, you can't count 'em.

The "Jamaican Study" also claimed grass-use had no connection with chromosome damage. Again, the facts. Out of the sixty cell cultures, twenty-seven didn't even grow! That simply means something was screwed-up either in preparing the samples or in the lab where they were tested.

Out of the thirty-three that did grow, way too few cells were looked at to tell anything. You usually need to examine at least 100 cells for each person studied. Of the cultures that grew, the researchers only counted between six and twenty-five cells. That's not enough cells for scientific accuracy.

It is possible the lab technicians wouldn't have known what to look for even if they did have enough cells. Most early studies looked for chromosome breaks. Recent experiments have shown that pot is more likely to cause abnormally low chromosome counts than chromosome breaks.[f]

In spite of the obvious shortcomings of the chromosome studies, "Ganja in Jamaica" still claimed there is no threat to this vital genetic material.

Brain testing also inconclusive.

"Ganja in Jamaica" said that years of pot smoking doesn't harm a person's mental abilities or personality. Here again, the facts don't back up the claim.

The study showed the farmers who used grass did just as well on intelligence and personality tests as the farmers who were straight. But these tests were designed to be used on Americans who are better educated and have a different way of life. On the average, the Jamaicans tested had a fourth-grade education. So could they really understand the tests they were given? If they didn't really understand the questions, smokers and non-smokers would both score so low there would, indeed, seem to be no difference in mental ability.

The researchers' personality tests were also designed for North Americans. The Jamaican natives gave answers that were different from the answers Americans would give. So the results of the tests weren't very reliable.

The medical part of the brain testing in this study was the EEG, the standard brain-wave test. We already discussed (in the chapter on marijuana and the brain) that regular surface tests have just recently started to show promise in marijuana research. In 1972, brain-wave tests did not routinely include giving the subjects a mental task. Recent breakthroughs propose that mentally challenging the subjects during testing may show dopers to be less alert. As the Jamaican brain tests were done, they didn't prove anything either way.

Jamaican doctors never bought it.

"Ganja in Jamaica" was never accepted by the scientific community of Jamaica. In 1974, a leading Jamaican doctor testified before the U. S. Senate. Dr. John Hall, chief of Jamaica's largest hospital, disagreed with every aspect of the study. Dr. Hall made the following comments when questioned by the Senate analyst, David Martin:

Martin: . . . Do you know anything about this study?

Hall: Yes, I am familiar with it.

Martin: Do the implications of this study . . . conform to your own experience with thousands of marijuana smokers?

Hall: That is correct. The study to which you refer does not have the general support of experienced clinicians and other workers in the field. We believe that the selection with which the study was done was faulty and that in regard to the reported absence of any change in the chromosome pattern that their technique was faulty and that certainly as regards the statement that there was no respiratory effect, it is unfounded.

Martin: From your experience and contacts you believe that the great majority of doctors in Jamaica who have had actual experience with marijuana smokers — ganja smokers — are convinced that it has a substantial negative effect?

Hall: That is correct.[4]

Most doctors in Jamaica think drug abuse is a serious health problem. They see people every day for various reasons, so they know a lot of dope smokers and know the smokers' health histories. From the experience of Dr. Hall, emphysema, bronchitis, digestive problems, sexual failure, and serious mental disorders are common problems of heavy ganja smokers.

In summary, practially all the conclusions of "Ganja in Jamaica" are invalid. Newer marijuana research has made this study completely outdated.

We looked at the Jamaican study mainly because it's a famous study that many people still believe in. It also proves you need all the facts to know the whole story. And as little as the Jamaica study really tells us, it was still part of the search for the perfect study.

Many other studies have been done; more are on the drawing board. Earlier in this chapter, we mentioned some of the "bugs" that are being worked out of newer marijuana studies. The experiments of the 80s will add greatly to the first ten years of serious marijuana research.

Much has been learned during the 70s. The "all-clear" flag on dope can no longer be waved. Any new research that claims marijuana is not a health risk to millions of Americans has a tough job. Such "nothing-to-worry-about" findings can only have real clout if they somehow manage to explain away the massive evidence that marijuana interferes with many body systems. That seems very unlikely.

Better designed, highly refined studies will tell us more about what, where, how, and how much grass disrupts normal body functions. The question of "whether or not it does" is as much an antique as gasoline at fifty cents a gallon.

Putting
It All
Together

decisions
along the
road to
better health

A Debate

There's a debate going on: Is marijuana ever useful as a medicine? Some doctors say pot can help cancer patients take medications without getting sick. Some see grass as an aid to people with a certain kind of eye problem. Still others believe the whole debate is a publicity stunt by the multi-billion dollar dope industry. Here are some facts on the debate.

THC WEAKENS VOMITING REFLEX

Many people with cancer receive chemotherapy, drugs given to try and cure cancer. These powerful drugs are actually poisons, scientifically designed to kill cancer cells quicker than they kill healthy cells. Problems of chemotherapy patients include nausea and vomiting.

THC, one of marijuana's 400 chemicals, weakens the brain's usual message to vomit when a person is poisoned. So not surprisingly, some cancer patients say THC reduces the sick feeling that chemotherapy causes.[1] However, knocking out the brain's vomiting center in a healthy person could be dangerous as it could weaken the natural defenses against accidental poisoning or drug overdose.

It must also be mentioned that marijuana does absolutely nothing to prevent or cure cancer. If anything, pot weakens the body's defenses against cancer. Even where THC has been used with cancer patients, problems such as dizziness and low blood pressure have been caused by the marijuana treatments.[2] Also, some doctors believe other drugs are more effective than pot in soothing the nausea and vomiting from chemotherapy.[3] So the debate goes on, and the issue is far from settled.

A DISEASE OF HIGH EYE PRESSURE

The eyes contain a fluid that keeps them round and solid. For good eye health, the pressure of the eyes must be normal. In the same way, automobile tires must have proper pressure to run well.

Sometimes the eye fluid pressure goes too high and causes a disease called glaucoma, a major cause of blindness. If the high eye pressure isn't corrected, the vision cells of the eye get crushed. If the disease is caught early on, blindness from glaucoma can be prevented with drugs that lower high eye pressure. (People over 40 should have their eyes checked yearly.)

The THC in marijuana lowers pressure inside the eyes, so it might be useful in treating glaucoma. Some doctors believe that THC treatments can help people with glaucoma.[4] Most eye specialists say that other drugs treat glaucoma better than pot and with fewer side effects.[5] Again, the debate continues.

Does marijuana's possible benefits for glaucoma patients mean that pot is good for your eyes? The answer is no.

The vast majority of people have normal eye pressure. Marijuana lowers the pressure in normal eyes, too. So for most people, a joint causes several hours of "spongy eyeballs." Just as tires low on air aren't especially safe, spongy eyeballs aren't such a hot idea, either. For example, if you got hit in the eye while stoned, your eye would have less fluid pressure to cushion the blow.

NO GREEN LIGHT FOR DOPERS

As we have mentioned, pot can knock out the brain's vomiting center and reduce eye pressure. Therefore, some of marijuana's 400 chemicals may eventually be used as medicines. Is that a green light for dopers? No way.

Many harmful drugs have certain medical applications. Morphine is sometimes used in hospitals as a pain killer. Throat specialists sometimes apply cocaine as a numbing agent. But people who use morphine or cocaine to get high still face the serious health hazards these drugs can bring about.

Much has been said about possible medical uses of marijuana. This debate is sure to continue for years. But the health risks from pot smoking still stand. And unless you need to soften your eyeballs or knock out your vomiting center, marijuana still offers just two things. The first is a momentary high, the second is a long list of health hazards.

Making Use of the Facts

Who's Got the Most to Lose?

The most obvious answer is *you*. However, it's riskier for certain people. For example, pregnant women, as we already mentioned, should definitely stay away from it. People with epilepsy run a greater risk of seizures.[a] People with heart disease should also pass it by, because marijuana is known to cause a slight strain on the heart.[b]

There are other important groups who could possibly be harmed by using marijuana. Children, quite obviously, should NOT smoke pot. When you think about all the ways that grass blocks the formation and growth of new cells, it makes no sense at all for them to have it! Remember, pot may be capable of causing brain damage. And a child's developing mind is too precious to gamble.

Teenagers also would be far better off without it. This makes special sense due to the growth and hormone changes during puberty. For example, a teen's rapid growth could possibly be stunted to some degree. Such a reaction certainly fits what we already know about marijuana. In addition, pot could very well have an unwanted affect on a teen's rapidly changing hormone levels. We have already mentioned that grass lowers several of the important hormones of puberty.

Another group of people who would probably not use it if they knew the facts are athletes, especially bodybuilders. This subject hasn't yet been looked into very much, but it makes sense. Dope hinders protein formation. Athletes want to build and strengthen muscles which are  mostly protein. With men, you have the added fact that "muscle building" requires normal testosterone levels. Lowered hormone levels (and decreased production of protein) won't help any man become "Mr. America."

If *half* of the things that look almost definite about dope today are proven beyond any doubt, dope will be shown to be a most expensive high — costly in terms of street price and human health.

Anything Else?

Tell you what. That's enough facts for now. Give them a little time to digest, to sink in. To repeat, all of the studies mentioned here are published in leading medical journals.

Just in case you've never heard any of this stuff before, don't feel bad. The public is just starting to hear of these findings.

We're reaching a point in medical research where more and more scientists will be speaking out about pot's effects on health. A lot of the question marks are starting to clear up as scientists design and run better and better experiments. Still, there is a great deal we just don't know.

In other words, you have to make up your own mind. Carefully read this book and decide for yourself what to do about grass. Show it to your doctor or scientist friends. Maybe they could read some of the technical information for you. You owe it to yourself to get the facts and add them up.

Human Guinea Pigs?

We've discussed quite a few new discoveries about marijuana and health. Also, we've made it clear that what it all means for pot smokers is not completely known.

For instance, some of the changes dope can cause in the lungs, the brain, the glands, or the blood cells might be reversible. That means they might go back close to normal by laying off the weed. On the other hand, the changes might prove to be permanent. We'll know for sure in about thirty years.

If you think about it, many of the folks walking around with lung cancer today were yesteryear's cigarette guinea pigs. Nobody told them then what smoking did, because nobody knew.

The full medical impact of pot-smoking on the health of America will be proven far in the future. Over the next few generations, scientists will examine many thousands of long-term grass users and their children. Then they'll have many answers where now they have only an educated guess.

Like it or not, every present-day smoker is a *human guinea pig*. If you smoke pot, you are testing a still unknown drug *on yourself*. If you toke up, you are part of the experiment.

Do Black Lungs Scare Anybody?

Everyone's seen pictures of the horrifying tar-filled lungs from years of tobacco smoking. Someday we'll know exactly what grass does to the lungs. But that's not the point.

The point is this: If everybody knows about what cigarettes do to you, why do so many people smoke them? Quitting any bad habit requires two steps: You've got to think about it and then do something about it. If we let all good advice go in one ear and out the other, we may as well have rocks for brains.

This message applies to people of all ages — kids, teens, grown-ups, senior citizens. If we hear good advice and we know it's true, then we should follow it. Who needs rocks for brains?

Everybody knows talk is cheap. It's like the old story we've all heard: People are ready to tell others what's good for them but less willing to take their own suggestions.

Rationalizing

You know, it's easy to rationalize — to think up excuses for anything we want to do. But when we convince ourselves to do things we really feel are not right for us, are we actually fooling anyone? When people rationalize, isn't it more like *ir*rationalizing?

Who Needs Drugs, Anyway?

Drugs have been with us for thousands of years. Used as medicines, many drugs have provided great benefit to the human race.

On the other hand, unwise use of intoxicating drugs has plagued many civilizations. A well-known example is the continuing problem of alcoholism among North American Indians.

Any Cheers for Clear Heads?

A famous comedian has said, "I don't get no respect." In many circles, those who choose *not* to alter their minds with drugs "don't get no respect."

It's not unusual to hear folks brag about how messed up they got or how late they partied. You rarely hear anyone brag about staying up late to study extra hard. It's tough to make sense out of it. If people are going to take pride in something, how about their work, how about their service to others?

Does the ability to "Scorch your brains until it rains" make a "real man" or a "real woman"? Does pot *really* make you feel better about yourself, or do you only feel good when you toke?

Let's hear some cheers for clear heads! It's about time they got more respect.

Natural Highs

Some of you will probably think a natural high is a big joke. Some of you will say, "Get high without drugs? What a laugh!" To others, however, it will make sense.

No matter what drug you take, they're all like putting on a different color of sunglasses. Booze will shade things one way. Speed will give things a different color, a different tint. The same for downers, pot, you name it.

No matter how much of a *tint, fuzz,* or *buzz* a drug puts on your outlook, you are still looking at life. Life is all there is, but it's quite a lot!

The next page offers some ideas for natural highs, to which you can add your own. You'll also notice that all the highs mentioned are ordinary, everyday events. To be sure, making a great scientific discovery, rescuing someone who is drowning, or winning the Superbowl would be very high moments. But how many of us can play quarterback for the Pittsburgh Steelers?

Usually, it's the simple pleasures that remind us how nice life can be. The gentle smile, the kind word, and the helping hand are often the highest moments of any day. These pleasures are for all to give and all to enjoy.

Listen to Your Heart

There is something within us that makes us search for meaning in our lives. We try this, we try that. But we're always looking for another clue to better enjoy and better understand life. And there's a little voice inside that always seems to be two steps ahead of us. Some people say, "Listen to your conscience." They really mean, "Listen to your heart."

It may sound *corny*. It may sound *unscientific. But doesn't it maybe make sense?*

The brain knows the rules
The ♥ knows the score
The brain knows alot
But the ♥ knows more

Won't You Be Free?

The Big Question — to toke or not to toke — is closely tied to the idea of freedom.

The word *freedom* sounds pretty. It has a nice ring to it. But what does it mean?

America is said to be a free nation. Indeed, we are free to become whatever we choose. But staying free means keeping our dreams alive.

If we let a dream die, if we fail to do what needs to be done, we are no longer free to make it come true.

Let's say you want to become a teacher, and you know you've got what it takes. But if you flunk out of school, the dream dies. You've lost the freedom to make it come true.

A country can lose its freedom. It can be attacked from outside. If a nation's defense is weak, attackers can bust in and say, "That's it! Now we're running the show."

A person can lose freedom by an attack from within. If foreign chemicals floating around the brain "run the show," is that person free?

If what pops into your mind when you want to enjoy yourself is, "I should get high first," your freedom is in danger. For example, you might think about playing frisbee. But before you reach for the frisbee, you'll think about playing it stoned. *That's the warning sign.* Someday you may only think about playing frisbee stoned. What ever happened to just playing frisbee?

When you start to get such a one-track mind, you're starting to get programmed. At that point you've lost some of your freedom.

In many ways, getting into dope can be like painting yourself into a corner. You don't even notice it until you're in so far that it takes a major clean-up effort to get out. Just talk to people who have tried to quit drugs. Whether it's caffeine or heroin, they'll tell you it's a tough road to travel.

To some people, freedom means that anything goes. I believe that freedom means making smart choices. When we do what we really think is right, we're less likely to get painted into a corner we can't easily get out of. When we listen to the voice of reason (and not just to what everybody else says), we begin to toughen our willpower, our "inner muscles." With a strong willpower we can keep dreams alive; we can remain free to make them come true.

Think about the following example. Leon plays basketball for the Cougars. The Cougars believe they have a good shot at winning the league championship.

OK, everybody knows proper rest is one of the keys to successful sports training. So the night before the first game, it goes like this: A few friends stop by and say "Let's go get a quick pizza." Leon figures it won't hurt to bend the coach's "bedtime" curfew a bit, especially since he hadn't seen these guys much since practice began. "Besides," he says to himself, "I won't be out that late anyways."

To make a long story short, one thing leads to another and Leon ends up sneaking quietly past the dog and into his room at three A. M. Since people who miss school on game days can't play, he only gets a couple of hours sleep.

During the game, Leon plays lousy — He only makes two of ten shots from the field and one of four from the free throw line. He commits six turnovers and the coach tells him his grandmother could have done better. The Cougars lose, 53 to 51.

Did Leon blow the game by not getting enough rest the night before? No way of telling, but the thought definitely crosses his mind. Who knows, if the Cougars lose the championship by one game,

Leon's midnight pizza run could end up as the most important play of the season.

Maybe this example seems a little far fetched. But it goes to show how little choices can later turn out to be major decisions. In the same way, the answer to "You wanna get high?" can be a mighty big decision in the long run.

So, stand up and be counted! Exercise your freedom! Keep your dreams alive! When it's right to say yes, do it! But be free to say "No." It's all right to say "No."

Again, won't you be free?

Summary

This book weaves together two different stories. First, the most recent and most important medical findings have been presented. You've read about what these experiments might mean for everyday people. Second, the book has also tried to get a handle on things that often go along with smoking grass — the social side of it.

The Medical Story

As you surely gathered from the information presented in the scientific sections, not all scientists agree about grass. Therefore, it's hard to make clear, definite statements about how marijuana affects health.

But from what we know, here are some thoughts about the heatlh effects of marijuana. (Keep in mind that any time you squeeze a whole subject into a few sentences, you are bound to leave a few things out.) The following statements reflect the opinions of many scientists involved in studying marijuana. If you read some of the articles and books mentioned, I think you will find many of these viewpoints repeated often.

1. Knowing how THC (marijuana's main chemical) works is very important to understanding grass. THC rapidly finds its way into all the body's cells and remains in the body for at least several weeks. THC unquestionably interferes with the cell's building of proteins and DNA and RNA (the code of life).
2. Marijuana might be capable of causing changes in genes and chromosomes. There is good evidence both for and against genetic damage from marijuana. Many lab studies with cells have shown

that THC can cause abnormal chromosome structures. These lab studies have been difficult to prove in humans; evidence has been presented on both sides of the chromosome damage question.

3. Marijuana somewhat weakens the immune system. Exactly how, however, is not well understood. It has clearly been shown that marijuana smoke can "paralyze" the defense cells within the lungs, one of the body's first lines of defense.

4. Marijuana smoke clearly can damage the lungs. The most recent information indicates it is more harmful than tobacco smoke. By chemical analysis, by the effect on individual lung cells, by animal studies and human studies, it seems obvious that "anything cigarettes can do to the lungs, a joint can do better."

5. To say marijuana causes brain damage sounds scary. So far, doctors don't know if it does for sure. Still, current evidence shows brain damage from long-term smoking looks possible. THC clearly builds up in brain cells — possibly causing permanent changes, especially in the deep brain areas controlling alertness and emotions. New brain-wave evidence suggests that toking several times a week causes a person to be mentally sluggish.

    Even if one should entirely discount the physical evidence of brain damage, reports from hundreds of psychiatrists cannot be ignored. They report these personality problems common to many chronic users: Poor memory, loss of willpower and motivation, lack of energy, paranoia, and mistrust.

6. Marijuana smoking has a definite unwanted effect on hormones. In men, long-time heavy use lowers testosterone levels and sperm counts, as well as causing more abnormal sperm. Each joint lowers testosterone levels for several hours.

    In both men and women, THC interferes with pituitary hormones that control sexual function (LH and FSH drop for several hours after toking).

    Pot smoking is an extremely poor idea for pregnant women. Daily toking during pregnancy increases a woman's risk of losing her child before birth. Doctors are also concerned about the mental development of children born to mothers who use pot.

7. Is marijuana addictive? It seems to fill many of the standard requirements. Physical tolerance develops, long-term users need greater amounts and/or stronger pot. Withdrawal symptoms have been reported in some studies.

8. Driving while stoned is as dangerous as driving while drunk, maybe more so. This fact has been proven many times over.

9. All these effects, except the decrease in driving skill, are largely invisible to the user. All these changes happen gradually; the user is not necessarily aware of them. In addition, most young smokers are healthy enough, just by being young, that it takes a lot more damage for them to notice any slowing down of body functions.

The Social Story

And what about this book's other intention, to help people understand a little more about the world of dope smoking? Mostly I want to say, "Make up your own mind."

Life is sometimes tough that way. We have to make our own decisions. Sometimes, the decisions we have to make will affect a lot of things down the line. For example, whether you to to college, get married or get a job can be pretty serious decisions. Deciding whether or not to smoke dope is also a big decision.

All these big decisions can be handled in one of two ways. We can do our best to figure out what is involved and try to make a smart choice. Or we can act like everything is one big party and not care what happens to us.

Even at a party, however, we still will make decisions. Some are easy. Some are not easy. Some things at parties are great ideas, while other things just don't make much sense.

At a party, you see the same kind of forces at work on people as in the everyday world. You see people doing things to be different or to be like everyone else. You see people trying to make others act like them. You see folks so confused, they don't know which end is up. There are all kinds, including show-offs and wallflowers.

You see things that are really funny, things that are only funny on the surface, and things that aren't funny at all. You see people hiding from their problems, people hiding from themselves, and others letting it all hang out.

So the next time you go to a party, think about how much it resembles the outside world. Look at the scene on the next page. See if some of these goings on don't remind you of decisions, large or small, that you have had to make.

Passing the Word

So, you've read about what the scientists think — the current research findings on marijuana. If you find much of this information hard to believe, just check the resources listed. After all, a majority of the general public has likely not heard of these findings.

Undoubtedly, some of you already knew about the new research. Some of you might have already suspected that marijuana was not a cure-all to life's problems. Maybe you smoke pot and you're concerned about what it's doing (or could be doing) to your health or the health of friends and family. What do you do?

Obviously, you could quit smoking pot. A test of a couple months without it could tell you a lot. You could see if you feel better. You could also discover, firsthand, whether you've come to depend on marijuana, whether you've become hooked to any degree.

So far as your friends are concerned, however, you can't quit something for them. No matter what you think about a subject, the next person must add up her or his own facts. The best approach is to share the facts, to "pass the word."

It's important that people have a realistic picture of marijuana. It's not a candy-coated dream, nor is it a hopeless nightmare. If more and more people smoke it based on the belief that its totally harmless, however, this country could well have a nightmare on its hands.

Just look back on the history of tobacco smoking. It took over eighty years of research to prove without a doubt that cigarettes cause lung cancer. Modern research equipment wasn't available then and the proof didn't come out until 1963.[a] Much earlier, though, it was painfully obvious to any scientist who didn't work for tobacco companies. By that time, people grew up believing that cigarettes were not harmful. When scientists were sufficiently convinced to sound the alarm, smoking cigarettes was already part of daily life. People are slow to quit habits once they get established, even bad habits.

Do we see the same pattern emerging with marijuana? In the United States, grass has risen in popularity for almost twenty years. The scientists who spoke out on damaging effects ten years ago were shouted down by people who were having too much fun smoking to think about possible health hazards. Finally, the research is becoming strong enough to withstand even "cheap-shot" criticism.

But how much a part of our culture has marijuana become? As we all know, mere facts are often weak arguments against established habit patterns or accepted customs. Perhaps, then, for the health and well-being of all Americans, we should *STAMP OUT DOPE!*

Can We Stamp Out Dope?

Even if almost everybody believes something is bad, even if that belief is based on solid data, it's near impossible to just *STAMP* something *OUT*. First, you have individual free will to contend with. People will do their own thing.

Even if the medical picture continues to grow more and more positive that pot has potential for serious damage, could we just stop people from using it? The government may as well stamp out *CRIME*, or stamp out *GREED*. Sounds good, but things usually aren't that simple.

An increase in drug use represents more of a symptom than the whole problem. Drugs are just the tip of the iceberg. (That means there's a bigger problem floating underneath!) What, then, does the iceberg of marijuana fever look like?

That's a very good question. The answer is obviously mixed up with heavy topics like personal fulfillment, sense of purpose, and the meaning of life.

How can we help uncover and deal with this "iceberg"? Must we all become psychiatrists in order to lend a hand? In all due respect, I surely hope not!

A good sense of the facts can definitely go a long way. Most people will listen to reason, especially if you're reasonable. Part of changing people's minds means that people must understand what you're saying. For example, a third grader can't read well enough to understand this book, but elementary schoolchildren still need to know the new findings about dope.

Think about this, too. If peer pressure starts some people smoking, it may also get them to stop. Once your friends understand what is known about grass, they'll know they have to make a tough decision. Most assuredly, many students reading this book will bring their friends up-to-date on this story. Certainly they will "pass the word."

"I Smoke Dope, and I Feel Great."

Some dopers won't be phased by the idea that dope affects their health. Long after pot is widely understood as a threat to health, we will still hear, "Hey, I smoke dope and I feel great." To that logic one can only reply, "Congratulations, I'm glad you are feeling well."

The plain fact is, health is more than skin deep. You may feel okay now — you may brag, "I'm in top shape" — but bad habits take their toll sooner or later. For example, there's the cigarette smoker who had just a little "smoker's cough." Six months later, the doctors called it lung cancer. Cancer takes years to develop; it doesn't happen overnight. During the cancer-forming process, most people feel fine. They may even say they feel great.

This whole concept, that serious disease takes time to happen, is worth keeping in mind when considering marijuana. When health begins to go downhill, few people notice. They can adjust to gradual changes. It's like those people who find out they need glasses years after they really needed them. The change is so gradual, they don't even notice it.

Could someone whose immune system, brain, or lungs were beginning to show damage from marijuana really expect to notice it? It's not likely.

Another question to ask is, would this person care? After all, healthy attitudes and common sense are very closely related.

What Does Dope Have in Common with Junk Food, Beer Bellies, and Tobacco Stains?

When you think about it, quite a bit. The common denominator of all these bad habits is attitude. In basic ways, similar attitudes about health form the groundwork for each of these habits.

First off, everybody knows junk food, alcohol, and cigarettes aren't good for you. If you've read this far, you know marijuana belongs in the same category. People are truly aware that when they smoke a joint, drink a beer, or eat a cream-filled Twink-Ho they're doing something wrong to their bodies.

These people reason that the damage is a fair trade for the pleasure. Since they don't notice how these habits are wearing down the body, the bad part of the "deal" is easily forgotten.

The "sugar-binge," the "all-night drunk," or the "bong-a-thon" are felt to be enjoyable. If it's "fun," it must be worth it. Right?

What's fun is entirely up to each of us. Still, is the fun from a pack of cigarettes each day a fair trade for lung cancer? To help make the point, let's get even further off the track. Think about your car.

People understand cars. They know how to take care of them. Most people practice long-term preventive care of their cars. They don't wait for the engine to explode before they check the oil.

They know keeping the engine well-tuned, "purring like a kitten," will head-off trouble before it starts. They know it's a bad bet to drive with dirty oil, worn spark plugs, or improperly aligned wheels. So they check those things out beforehand.

It's the old story — "You can pay me now, or pay me later." The "ounce of prevention" cliche definitely fits. It makes sense and people believe it.

But the connection between cars and human bodies is not grasped by many today. They might take care of their auto but not their health.

In ancient China, doctors were only paid if their patients stayed healthy. What if we did that today? Doctors would probably be after you all the time to be more careful with yourself.

The most important aspect of preventive care is attitude. With their cars, people are usually unwilling to compromise. When they hear an engine knock, they check it out. If they don't, trouble is often close behind.

Our bodies, however, don't always tell us when we are fouling something up. That's part of the problem with taking care of them. The human body is a very tough machine. We can abuse it, we can let it slide out of shape. More often than not, it bounces back, ready for more.

That is where attitude plays a vital role. If we buy the "live for the moment" attitude about health, anything goes. Quite often, our health also goes. Junk food instead of vegetables, a six-pack after dinner, and a big, fat joint for dessert, make sense only if we disregard long-term consequences as being important.

Realistically, one chocolate scrunge-bun won't do much damage. The same goes for one beer. But because one joint takes about a month to leave the body, it might be a different story. We might even say, for the sake of argument, that one joint's not that big of a deal — *unless, of course, it's the first one you ever smoke. Then it is a big deal.*

I'm not going to list here all the bad health habits a person can have and line them up from best to worst. Personally, I think medical researchers will someday be unanimous that marijuana is worse than either tobacco or alcohol. (Many leading scientists already feel there's no question about it.) Still, there's room for debate. But that's not my main point. What I really want you to think about is how *you* feel about it.

Any or all of these habits can be chosen in the name of fun or relaxation. Each joint can be considered just a "drop in the bucket," so far as effect on your health goes. The thing is, a lot of drops will eventually fill a bucket. (Maybe that's where the line about "kicking the bucket" comes in?)

Does all this suggest we must give up fun just for health's sake? Of course not! If we don't enjoy life, how could we possibly call ourselves healthy?

But we owe it to ourselves to ask, how much of our fun is actually a rip-off? Maybe each of us should think about how much of our fun is actually an invitation to poor health.

We could stand to re-examine our attitudes about how fun and health go hand-in-hand. And we all could take a few lessons from a well-tuned automobile engine.

It's a Matter of Vision

It has been said, "Without vision the people perish." Does this have any connection with the subject of marijuana? Yes.

There isn't a good way to prove it, but I think the vision of America — as a nation and as individuals — has changed over the last decade. I think it has become a little foggy, maybe a little lazy or apathetic.

Again, even if this is true, what's it got to do with marijuana smoking? Somewhere between everything and plenty.

Our *vision* is very important. It's a part of how we look at ourselves. It's like our self-image, except there is more to it.

This vision, commonly called "the mind's eye," takes account both of where we are and where we're heading. We all go through changes in life. If we know what we want ourselves to become, if we visualize those positive changes actually occurring, what we want to become will more than likely happen.

If we see ourselves as having glowing physical health, we're far more likely to do things that result in good health. If we see ourselves becoming strong and healthy, even if we have a way to go, we're more likely to avoid things that lead to poor health. Little by little, we become healthier.

A person who views himself as slim and trim doesn't gorge himself at the dinner table. So he pushes himself away after a sensible meal and doesn't get fat.

When someone declares, "I'm on a diet," but he really can't imagine his spare-tire melting away, that diet is doomed to failure. Unless that person truly envisions the diet as working and has real confidence in it, there is a missing ingredient to success.

The power of vision is what got Christopher Columbus across the Atlantic Ocean. It's vaulted many brave women and men past barriers others said were too great. Each of us can use this talent to lead more fulfilling lives.

Back to marijuana. The question becomes, "What kind of vision fits with smoking grass?" A picture of health? Don't kid yourself.

As mentioned before, pot-smokers can be healthy, but not because they smoke pot. A person can be healthy *in spite of* grass, but never *because of it.*

Someday we'll know exactly what the health cost of marijuana use is. But today, the handwriting is already on the wall. Medical research is making the story clearer each day. Those who read the handwriting on the wall with a clear vision of health will say, "No thanks."

Who Needs a Pep-talk, Anyway?

From time to time, most everyone needs a pep-talk. I want to mention this fact because many folks seem to shy away from encouragement. If they hear an encouraging word, one that spurs them on to try harder, they call it a "sermon."

When you get right down to it, answers to most of our problems are very basic. It's usually not the fine points that trip us up, but the easy stuff. After we decide, "Ok, I *will* solve this problem," the rest follows. That first, basic step often spells the whole ballgame. Success in anything first requires the spirit, or the will, to succeed. The basics come first; details always follow.

If we stop talking about the basics, if we stop trying to make them part of our lives, they'll stop being part of our lives. Sometimes, the most obvious things are the ones we forget first.

After all, what's more obvious than a statement like "Love thy neighbor"? Of course it's a good idea. And it's so obvious, we probably don't try hard enough to work it into our lives. The same goes for things like unselfishness, hard work, and honesty. All of these ideas are obviously good ones. But we've got to work these ideas into our lives — work at them, talk about them. If we really believe in these ideas, we must make them part of our vision — for ourselves.

Perhaps the reason some folks can't handle encouragement — in other words, a "pep-talk" — is because they've lost faith in themselves. The fact that someone else has confidence in them "blows their minds." I think that people who know and believe in themselves can accomplish their goals. They merely need to believe they're worth the effort.

Closing Comments

This book presents many of the latest medical findings on marijuana. Beyond a shadow of a doubt, scientists now know that marijuana carries a health risk, perhaps a sizable one. With recent trends of escalating use, it is important that more people, especially young people, recognize pot-smoking as a documented health gamble. The research picture is far from complete, but there is already much we do know.

This book also tries to work out some of the larger questions. Namely, if smoking pot represents the tip of an iceberg, what is the iceberg?

What's underneath the water becomes far less mysterious with some plain old *common sense*. And clearly, common sense is drastically needed to deal with the marijuana issue.

Before we blindly wake up over our heads in dope, let's study and communicate the truth about marijuana. Before we blindly legislate, let us learn. Above all, let's reason it out together.

Other Good Books on the Subject

Nahas, G. G., *Keep off the grass — A scientific inquiry into the biological effects of marijuana.* New York: Pergamon Press (1979).

Dr. Nahas has probably done more than any other person to encourage scientific research on marijuana. In this book he helps readers to grasp the broad yet subtle range of this issue. Skillfully written, it conveys technical clarity and personal warmth. While sharpening the readers' scientific awareness, *Keep Off The Grass* peers firsthand at the unique pressures acting upon this research field.

Russell, G. K., *Marihuana today — A compilation of medical findings for the layman.* New York: The Myrin Institute for Adult Education (1978).

Dr. Russell has written a well-documented, no-nonsense paperback. He gets straight to the point: marijuana is a weighty medical hazard. A brief and excellent handbook for the serious student.

Marihuana: Biological effects — Analysis, metabolism, cellular responses, reproduction and brain. (Nahas, G. G., and Paton, W. D. M., eds.) Oxford: Pergamon Press (1979).

This hefty, highly technical volume covers Paris' 1978 international symposium on marijuana. The fifty papers presented, fully indexed and referenced, are fifty comprehensive chapters by acknowledged "heavyweights" in this research field. This book is easily the most up-to-date major work available. *Marihuana: Biological Effects* will probably form the nucleus of future marijuana research.

Marihuana research findings: 1976. National Institute on Drug Abuse, Research Monograph Series, #14 (Peterson, R. C., ed.). Washington, D. C.: U.S. Government Printing Office, U.S. Department of Health, Education, and Welfare (1977).

This government manual covers information available throughout 1976. It's an excellent source of reasonably current information. It is a broad scientific overview and is written in less technical style than formal research papers.

Includes a comprehensive listing of references. It can be ordered from the Superintendent of Documents, U.S. Government Printing Office, Washington, D.C., as DHEW Publication No. (ADM) 78-501.

Pharmacology of Marihuana (Braude, M.C., and Szara, S., eds.). New York: Raven Press (1976).

Marihuana: Chemistry, biochemistry and cellular effects (Nahas, C.G., ed.). New York: Springer-Verlag (1976).

These two technical works are similar to *Marihuana: Biological Effects.* Both contain key research papers not available elsewhere. They are important volumes for medical-oriented libraries.

Appendix:

What's Normal for NORML?

As you know, all the answers about marijuana aren't in yet. With all the old and new studies in print, anyone with any viewpoint can find some study to back it up. For instance, if a person were really down on jogging and really into pot, he could "prove" jogging was worse for one's health than pot. He could argue that people get pulled muscles and knee injuries from jogging. And he would then say that since hardly anyone wrenches a knee while rolling a doobie, jogging is worse for your health, right? Not exactly; and what's this idea got to do with NORML?

When telling a story, people often leave out the facts that don't fit their point of view. With this fact in mind, I would like to share with you some of my thoughts about the group, NORML (The National Organization for the Reform of Marijuana Laws).

Why should you know about NORML?

1. It is an active, well-known organization that deals solely with the subject of marijuana (the nation's largest such group).
2. According to NORML's widely read publications, the group feels marijuana isn't much of a health threat.
3. In my opinion, the medical information NORML gives is out of date and inaccurate.

Who is NORML?

The National Organization for the Reform of Marijuana Laws is a non-profit citizens' action group. Its goal is the removal of all criminal penalties for owning or using marijuana. It tries to influence, (or *lobby*) the state and federal lawmakers. It has gained support from many well-known individuals and organizations. NORML has played a leading role in removing criminal penalties for marijuana use in eleven states. The group also passes out information on the legal, social, and medical aspects of marijuana.

"Marijuana: The Facts"

What we're going to look at in this section is how up to date and reliable NORML's medical information is. Let's examine a recent NORML brochure. *Marijuana: The Facts* is a leaflet NORML published in January, 1979. In a section titled "Public Health and Safety," there are six quotes from a 1972 study by the National Commission on Marijuana and Drug Abuse[1] (the Shafer Commission). This report, also called the "President's Commission Study," was widely publicized. Some people believed it said that it was okay to legalize marijuana.

When the study was published, leading scientists did not feel it gave pot an "all-clear." Many felt it said, at most, that we just don't know enough about marijuana to call it either safe or terribly dangerous. Printed in 1972, the study was naturally limited by 1972 research findings — what's now "ancient history," so to speak. Even today, though, some people still consider this obviously outdated report as the final word on marijuana. The following six quotes are from the "President's Commission Study," reprinted in NORML's 1979 "Fact" leaflet.

Medical and Health Data:
1. "The most notable statement that can be made about the vast majority of marijuana users — experimenters and intermittent users — is that they are essentially indistinguishable from their nonmarijuana-using peers by any fundamental criterion other than their marijuana use." (p. 41)[a]
2. "From what is now known about the effects of marijuana, its use at the present level does not constitute a major threat to public health." (p. 90)[b]
3. "No conclusive evidence exists of any physical damage, disturbances of bodily processes, or proven human fatalities attributable solely to even very high doses of marijuana." (pp. 56-57)[c]
4. "Although a number of studies have been performed, at present no reliable evidence exists indicating that marijuana causes genetic defects in man." (p. 84)[d]
5. "No objective evidence of specific pathology of brain tissue has been documented. This fact contrasts sharply with the well-established brain damage of chronic alcoholism." (p. 85)[e]
6. "In a word, cannabis does not lead to physical dependence." (p. 87)[f]

All of these statements make marijuana look about as dangerous as a stuffed teddy bear, and this is the *only* medical information given in the pamphlet. Notice that in this 1979 pamphlet, NORML chose to use information from a 1972 report. Even though hundreds of experiments were published between 1972 and 1979, NORML chose not to mention any of them.

An Expert Sets the Record Straight

In 1974, the U. S. Senate held hearings on marijuana. Experts from around the world gave testimony. Among them was Dr. Henry Brill, one of four doctors that worked on the 1972 study that NORML quoted from. He said that everybody was forgetting about the part of the report that said much more research was needed and that people should be cautioned against pot's possible health damage.

Since Dr. Brill helped write the study from which all the medical information in NORML's pamphlet was taken, his opinions are central to the theme of this chapter. So here is part of what Dr. Brill actually told the U. S. Senate. (I've added italics to highlight some statements.)

> I am here today as an individual and not as a representative of any organization, but I was a member of the National Commission on Marihuana and Drug Abuse throughout its period of operation, and *I am concerned about the misinterpretations which have developed* with respect to the marihuana report of that Commission. *These misinterpretations result from reading the reassuring passages in the report and ignoring the final conclusions and recommendations,* and the passages in the report on which they were based. As a result *it has been claimed that the Commission's report was intended to give marihuana a clean bill of health,* and as a covert, or indirect support for legalization of this drug in the near future, or as a step in that direction. *Nothing could be further from the truth.*
>
> From my knowledge of the proceedings of the Commission I can reaffirm that the report and the subsequent statements by the Commission meant exactly what they said, namely that *this drug should not be legalized,* that control measures for trafficking in the drug were necessary and should be continued, and that use of this drug should be discouraged because of its potential hazards.[2]

* * * * *

> *Contrary to what has been claimed there never was any intention to indicate in the Commission's report that we already knew enough about marihuana in 1972 to justify its legalization.* Instead a major section of the report is devoted to the need for more research.[2]

* * * * *

> *Scientific reports which have become available since the report was written confirm still further the need for caution.* The newer data includes clinical reports which have continued to become available concerning complica-

tions of acute and chronic use: descriptions of mental deterioration and acute psychotic attacks after cannabis in reports from India; evidence of high incidence of impaired lung function; further data on flashbacks in LSD users which seem to be associated with subsequent marihuana use; and reports of acute psychotic reactions from even small amounts of cannabis in certain cases.[2]

* * * * *

Finally, one should note the comment from Jamaica in the West Indies where the effects of cannabis had been thought to be relatively benign; among the middle class it is now found to be associated with school dropouts, transient phychoses, panic states, and adolescent behavior disorders. In general the effects of the drug continue to be noted as subtle and insidious. I would like to emphasize that one way to describe the effect of cannabis: it is subtle and insidious, but harmful reactions in the heart and circulatory system are suspected, and there are indications of adverse reaction in the body's anti-infection chemistry.

Finally, some older issues are being reopened and evidence is that physical dependence does occur with very heavy use and that withdrawal leads to physical sickness in man and in animals. These are but a few illustrations chosen almost at random to show that the latest scientific literature strongly supports the cautionary position of the Commission. I may add that *in my own view marihuana must still be classed as a dangerous drug, dangerous to enough people to warrant full control.* I don't distinguish sharply between hashish and marihuana; these are different concentrations of the same principle.[2]

The Senate then asked Dr. Brill questions about how the report had been misquoted. Here's part of what was discussed:

Martin: You said you were concerned over the misinterpretations that developed with respect to the Shafer Commission report. I want to quote what you said, "These misinterpretations result from reading the reassuring passages in the report, and ignoring the final conclusions and recommendations."

Now, who was responsible for these misinterpretations, was it the media, was it the academic community, promarihuana pressure groups?

Brill: It is hard to point the finger at anybody, but I think there is a *great deal of wishful thinking involved: and a lot of people wish that this source of pleasure were completely harmless, and therefore it was rather easy to believe in it, and to shut off all negative information that might be available.*

Martin: You made the point, Dr. Brill, that the media in general covered the report of the Shafer Commission in a one-sided manner, that they ignored, or misrepresented in some cases the basic thrust of your report. Has this one-sidedness carried over to other areas? Would you agree or disagree, for example, with the chairman's opening statement, and I want to quote what he said, "There has been widespread publicity for writings and research advocating a more tolerant attitude towards mari-huana, while there has been little or no publicity for writings or research which point to serious adverse consequences."

Brill: As I read what is in the media, and hear it, I must admit that *the favorable side of marihuana is more heavily presented than the un-favorable side.* I can't agree with this kind of emphasis; I think it needs more balance. There have been both sides presented in many cases, but overall I am afraid that the statement is quite correct.

Martin: The chairman also said in his opening statement the purpose of these hearings was to present the other side, the side that by and large has not been heard by the Congress and the American people, so that both the Congress and people would have an understanding of both sides of this controversy.

Would you concur in the judgement that the presentation of the other side is badly needed?

Brill: I think it is. I think it needs to be emphasized. The Commission report, I thought, presented a fairly balanced picture; but what emerged from it, in the public consciousness, was quite unbal-anced. So, I would completely agree: *the negative side of this picture, the unpleasant side, has to be faced.*

Martin: The subcommittee has received evidence that noted scientists whose research and analyses pointing to serious adverse con-sequences have come under violent personal attack, including public and private harassment from members of promarihuana lobbies, and even members of the scientific community associ-ated with the promarihuana lobby. Do you have any personal knowledge of such attacks on fellow scientists?

Brill: I have seen this happen on several occasions, yes; I was quite distressed by it.[2]

In his final comments, Dr. Brill added:

. . . *My own personal opinion is that this is sufficiently unsafe, so that it should not be legalized.* There are some people who say that no drug is safe, all drugs are unsafe, all drugs are the same. I think this is misleading, and I think that this drug is unsafe for enough people, so that it should not be made generally available.[2]

From Dr. Brill's testimony, it doesn't sound like he would agree with the NORML brochure. In fact, Dr. Brill believes the quotes NORML selected for their pamphlet, "The Facts" gives a distorted picture of the study's intended message. He also believes the medical quotes in the pamphlet give a misleading idea of what scientists now know about marijuana.[8]

Old Quotes Never Die

Another example of what I think is "normal" for NORML comes from the same brochure. It quotes Dr. Robert DuPont, the director of the National Institute on Drug Abuse from 1973-1978. In 1975, Dr. DuPont said ". . . there is no question that alcohol and tobacco are causing us far more health problems than marijuana does."[3] That quote was printed in the "Fifth Annual Report to Congress." Several years later, NORML used his quote in its "The Facts" brochure.

But what NORML didn't mention was that in the Congressional report of 1976, Dr. DuPont was far less enthusiastic about pot than he was in 1975. Here's what he said then:

> If laboratory findings of possible effects on the body's immune re-sponse, endocrinologic functioning, and cell metabolism prove to have serious clinical implications, marijuana's persistence in the body may make even episodic use risky.[4]

Later, in 1978, Dr. DuPont was interviewed in the *U. S. News and World Report*.[h] Here are some of the comments he made (italics mine):

> Q: Do you expect other consequences from such widespread use?
> A: Yes, *so far we have only seen the tip of the iceberg*. We're going to see more evidence of the harmful consequences of marijuana use on health, social activities, family living and work performance as time goes by. *Those people going around today emphasizing the benignness [harmlessness] of marijuana are going to have a tough time with their consciences.*
>
> Q: Are there also health hazards to marijuana?
> A: Yes. The problem is in knowing exactly what the health conse-quences are. We now have a 4-million-dollar-a-year federal research pro-gram on marijuana, and we're learning more about it every year. But the nature of science is that scientists often contradict each other, and the most frequent finding in science is always uncertainty.
> In the area of effects of marijuana on the male sex hormone testoster-one, for example, *there is disagreement among scientists. So the promarijuana people say: "You see, there's no problem." In fact, marijuana does influence the hormone levels of the body, the body's immune response, the way we think and the tissues of the lung.* Bronchitis, for example, is common in people who smoke marijuana cigarettes. Furthermore, *there is laboratory evidence to show that marijuana is more likely to cause cancerlike lesions than in cigarette smoke.*
> It's going to take years to sort all that out. My point is this: We already know enough to say that marijuana poses a substantial risk. *Anybody who*

takes that drug and thinks that nothing is happening to his body has lost his mind. Marijuana is a powerful drug that is influencing his entire body.

The other thing people don't understand: Marijuana stays in your body for over a week from a single dose. If a person is only smoking marijuana once a week, his body is continuously exposed to THC — tetrahydrocannabinol, the major ingredient — all the time. That's not true for tobacco or alcohol. We don't know yet what the consequences of that are. But it isn't too bright to expose yourself to this risk.

Q: Do you think that many Americans underestimate the dangers of marijuana?

A: Absolutely. One of the most distressing facts to me has been the difficulty communicating the risks of marijuana use. Probably no issue was more frustrating to me in five years as director of the National Institute on Drug Abuse. . . .[5]

So these are Dr. DuPont's current opinions about pot, information that was available to NORML. Yet NORML chose to use his 1975 statement, a viewpoint that Dr. DuPont doesn't believe in anymore. (Interestingly, today Dr. DuPont is *against* removal of all criminal penalties for possession of marijuana.[6,i] Removal of penalties, also called *decriminalization*, is the major goal of NORML's efforts.)

Actions Speak Louder than Words

NORML's official policy is that the group does not promote the use of marijuana. In 1975, the director of NORML said before the U. S. Senate, "I want quickly to disavow the tendency of people to consider NORML a pro-pot lobby."[7] He also said, "We are not attempting to encourage use; and, in fact, we support discouragement toward all recreational drug use and that includes tobacco and alcohol, as well as marijuana."[7] NORML's "Official Policy" statement also says that the group discourages abuse of all drugs, including marijuana.[j]

But actions always seem to speak louder than words. The UPI wire service carried a story on October 29, 1979 titled "Marijuana Festival Celebrates Grass Cult Politics, Products." It described "the nation's first marijuana festival."[8]

This three-day convention in San Francisco featured a booth that gave a free bong to the fastest joint roller. The "Libertarian Party" also gave free joints to new members. The extravaganza was sponsored by none other than — you guessed it — NORML. (By my way of thinking, a group that wanted to discourage drug abuse *would not* sponsor a three-day dope convention.)

What NORML wants to say, or promote, or sell is strictly their business. What's "normal" for NORML, each person must decide. But it's apparent to me that NORML wants to make marijuana look as harmless as possible. (Laws to remove marijuana penalties must be easier to obtain with that outlook.) And as far as medical information goes, their most recent publications make NORML look like a most *un*reliable source.

Glossary of Dope Terms

To understand anything about dope, "ya gotta rap the right lingo." All these words below have something to do with getting stoned. There are undoubtedly many popular terms not mentioned. But this list covers enough of the main ones to give you a good idea of "what's goin' down where the green grass burns."

Words that mean . . .

Marijuana	pot, grass, reefer, weed, hooka, dope, rope, ganja, Kong, hemp, Mary Jane, smoke
Marijuana cigarette	joint, jay, reefer, bone, doobie, splif, Kong-Stick, number
High on pot	stoned, buzzed, ripped, wasted, fried, scorched, cooked, messed-up, blitzed
Inhale a joint	toke, take a hit, draw, poke, turn on
Roll a joint	roll, twist, crank one
Light a joint	light-up, fire one up, stoke one
Good pot	Sinsemilla, Colombian, Acapulco Gold, Jamaican, Panama Red, Hawaiian, Vietnamese

Bag, lid	a standard amount of pot for sale, usually about three-quarter ounce.
Bong	a modified water pipe, designed to draw a large amount of water-cooled smoke. Also, to smoke a bong, as in "do a bong".
Bong-juice	the water that cools the smoke in a bong. When it gets raunchy from not being cleaned, this is the actual meaning of the term. A real treat if spilled on the carpet.
Brownies	a way to take dope by mouth. Pot is finely ground and baked in brownies or cookies. In reality, a less efficient way to take THC than smoking, as the gut absorbs far less THC than lungs. Usually, a good amount of pot is used per batch.
Burnout	someone who is *burned out* on pot; a person who can't talk or think about anything but dope.
Busted	arrested on a drug-related charge, usually for selling drugs.
Cannabis	the scientific name for pot.
Dealer	someone who sells grass or other drugs for profit.
Ditch weed	low-potency wild-grown marijuana.
Dry	the state of being without reefer.

Hash
: a marijuana extract that is compressed into chunks. Some hash is stronger than good pot, but now most hash is weaker than good reefer.

Heavy burner
: a person who smokes a lot of dope. Such people are often experienced smokers who have developed tolerance to the effects. In other words, many heavy burners actually need more pot to get high.

Munchies
: a strong desire to eat that often comes along with getting stoned. More often than not, people with munchies prefer to gorge themselves with junk food.

Roach
: a "butt" left from a joint, high in THC.

Roach clip
: a special holder, usually with a handle, for smoking roaches.

Score
: to locate and purchase a quantity of marijuana.

Shotgun
: you "give a shotgun," or "get a shotgun". The person giving a shotgun holds the lit end of the joint in his mouth and then blows a large cloud of smoke out the unlit end. Requires great skill.

Stems and seeds   the bottom of the bag; the dregs; what's left when the pot is all smoked up. Most people that smoke stems and seeds are desperate to get high.

THC   the main chemical in marijuana. The percent THC in pot runs from less than 1 percent in ditch weed to over 5 percent in Sinsemilla or Colombian Gold. THC is also a name for a very bogus street drug, PCP. Real THC is *never* sold on the street.

Water pipe   a pipe that draws the smoke through water in order to cool the smoke.

Study Notes

You Wanna Get High?

A. Marijuana is a complex substance composed of around 400 known chemical compounds. Sixty of these compounds are found only in the cannabis (marijuana) plant and are called *cannabinoids*. The better-known cannabinoids include delta-9-THC (tetrahydrocannabinol), delta-8-THC, cannabinol (CBL), cannabidiol (CBD), and cannabichromene (CBN).

B. According to a 1977 government report on marijuana use, the following percentages of Americans (by age groups) have tried grass:

Age	Percent
14-15	29%
16-17	47%
18-21	59%
22-25	62%
26-34	44%
35 +	7%

C. According to a 1978 pamphlet by the U. S. Department of Health, Education and Welfare (*Highlights from Drugs and the Class of '78*), the percent of graduating seniors (nationwide) who smoked pot daily are as follows:

Class of	Percent
1975	6.0%
1976	8.2%
1977	9.1%
1978	10.7%

D. When scientists use the term *THC*, they usually mean delta-9-THC. It's the chemical most responsible for the high — and major health effects. However, there are technically many other "THC" compounds. When THC is mentioned in this book, it will mean delta-9-THC.

E. Much of the information about street pot comes from government tests on grass seized during drug busts. For example, the University of Mississippi has had a government contract since 1970 to run tests on marijuana captured by federal drug agents.

According to Dr. Carlton E. Turner, on staff at the university's pharmacy school, the delta-9-THC content of street pot now runs over four percent. Some shipments average almost ten percent delta-9-THC.

Much of the dramatic increase in strength of American pot comes from the recent sale of more Colombian Gold and Sinsemilla (an unpollinated "super-reefer") than in past years. (To compare grass with hashish, the current average hashish sold here contains about two percent delta-9-THC.)

F. *High Times* is a monthly magazine devoted to the subject of "leisure drugs," such as pot and cocaine. Their format includes articles on how to buy, grow, process, sell, and experience better drug highs. Most of the advertisers feature drug-related items (such as bongs, roach clips, coke spoons, and rolling papers). Over one-half million people read *High Times*. Similar publications include *Head* and *Hi-life*.

G. PCP is the abbreviation for *phencyclidine hydrochloride*. PCP was developed during the 1950s as a surgical anesthetic. Its use was discontinued when one-third of the patients woke up screaming after surgery. PCP is now understood to be a powerful hallucinogenic drug (like LSD). Now its only legal use is as an anesthetic for animals. (However, since PCP also has violent and unpredictable effects on animals, it is being replaced by more effective, less dangerous drugs.)

The National Institute on Drug Abuse says the use of PCP is increasing more rapidly than any other street drug. It is estimated that about seven million Americans have tried the drug. (The average age of a PCP user is fourteen.) About one of every six junior high and high school students in New York City has tried PCP.

An excellent documentary on PCP has recently been completed. "Angel Death," narrated by Paul Newman and Joanne Woodward, has been televised in many cities. The film gives medical facts and also tells the story of many PCP users — some of whom killed and mutilated friends in bizarre manners while under the drug's influence.

PCP is easy to overdose on. Just a little PCP causes hallucinations and an agitated state. Higher doses act as a strong depressant, causing zombie-like staring into space. A mere touch more can send a person into convulsions, coma, and sometimes death.

One research team is currently studying the effects of PCP on the brain cells of monkeys. The work has just begun, but early reports suggest that PCP easily lives up to its reputation as a drug capable of causing serious damage in small amounts.

It's a Matter of Chemistry

A. There are two main body organs — the liver and the lungs — that change THC into other chemicals of the THC family. As the body tries to deactivate the drug, these organs create literally hundreds of different chemical products — which further complicate the study of grass. Eating grass (rather than smoking it) produces slightly different chemical products for the body to handle.

B. The body burns up alcohol at a constant rate, regardless of how much is drunk. Six hours is an average amount of time required to completely "burn up" a drink. Depending on the person and the amount drunk, complete elimination of alcohol may require up to twelve hours.

C. THC is extremely *fat soluble* (it loves fat!). Therefore, THC dissolves rapidly in oily liquids (like animal fats or vegetable oils), and dissolves poorly in watery liquids (like blood). Within minutes after THC enters the bloodstream, it begins moving toward more comfortable surroundings (like body tissues rich in fat and cell membranes throughout the body).

D. As THC is drawn from the blood to body areas richer in fat (where THC is more comfortable), it makes the cell membranes its target. Because the cell membrane (the "skin" surrounding each cell) is rich in fat, THC can "lock in" to the membrane. The wall of the nucleus (the heart of a cell) is also rich in fat, and it is another target for THC. In fact, since THC swims well through fat, it can affect virtually every cell and each part of the cell.

Because the brain, liver, heart, kidneys, lungs, and glands contain much fat, THC builds up in these areas. In this way THC is much like the poison DDT, which collects in the body with repeated exposure because it is attracted to fat.

E. The *pharmacokinetics* (the study of how the body handles drugs) of THC is not completely understood in human users. How does it build up, and how long does it take to leave? For example, the idea that it takes one month to eliminate the THC from one joint was determined by studies using dogs. It has been proven that dogs handle THC elimination very much like humans; recent limited studies on people suggest that the body needs several weeks to get rid of the dope from one joint.

The concept of THC build-up in regular users is not surprising in light of THC's strong attraction to fat. Regular exposure to most fat-soluble drugs usually does cause build-up.

Here's what happens: Within an hour after smoking a joint, most of the THC has worked out of the blood. That doesn't mean it's gone — it's just stored in the cells, which slowly release THC back into the blood. This slow release is the reason dope stays in the body for weeks. Daily users may have ten times as much THC in their bodies as once-a-month users.

F. The concentrations of THC used in cell culture experiments is in the range of *parts per thousand* of THC. These levels can only be consistently reached in humans by heavy, daily use. However, certain cells and body parts are far more sensitive to THC. For example, the pituitary gland will decrease hormone production when exposed to parts per *million* THC. The hypothalamus, which controls much of the pituitary, is affected by amounts of THC as small as several parts per *billion* (amounts reached by one hit of good reefer).

Marijuana and the Lungs

A. The results of this forty-seven day-test, run at UCLA College of Medicine, suggest that daily heavy smoking causes a narrowing of the breathing passages. This narrowing arises from the swelling of tissue lining caused by smoke irritation.

Both large and small air passages were involved. An increase in *airway resistance* and a decrease in *specific airway conductance* indicated the problems in large airways. Narrowing of the small airways was reflected in increased *closing volumes* and markedly decreased *maximal midexpiratory flow rate* (how fast air can be blown out of the lungs).

In addition, special radioisotopic scanning tests were run on seven of the seventeen subjects. This highly sensitive test showed lung abnormalities from heavy smoking that were not detected by other tests.

B. Lung damage involved a severe inflammatory response, which became more severe as the experiment progressed. The technical description of the damage was a focal pneumonitis, which progressed to a pronounced proliferative (abnormal growth) condition, associated with focal granulomatous and cholesterol clefts. Rats exposed to an equal amount of tobacco smoke showed far less serious lung damage.

C. Carcinogenic hydrocarbons are the hydrocarbons that cause cancer. Marijuana smoke contains more of them than tobacco smoke. (Technically, polynuclear hydrocarbon fractions are the chemicals in question.) There are also many naturally occurring hydrocarbons that do not cause cancer.

D. To get the most for their money, dopers hold the smoke in as long as they can. This practice not only gives the best high — it also allows the maximum opportunity for cancer-causing hydrocarbons to eat away at lung cells.

E. Many tokers prefer to use "double-wide" papers for easier rolling and slower, more even burning of the joint. Double-wide papers, however, produce more pollutants to be breathed in with the marijuana smoke.

F. THC is attracted to lung tissue because of the tissue's high fat content. Its first shot at the lungs is on its way in with the smoke irritants. It gives the lungs a second pass as it leaves the blood stream when the high fades away.

G. A Harvard University research team tested how well rats could fight off *staph* germs, bacteria that can cause disease in humans. In the lungs, cells called *macrophages* "eat" breathed-in bacteria. Rats forced to breathe dope smoke were less able to fight the staph germs. The stoned rats couldn't defend themselves as well, due to the slowing down of their lung macrophages (which occurs after smoking a joint).

H. Dr. Forest S. Tenant, head of the U. S. Army's drug program in Europe from 1968 to 1972, studied the high number of breathing complaints among soldiers stationed in Germany. He used the term *hashish bronchitis* to describe the breathing disorder he found in a high number of hash heads. He also saw another serious problem, emphysema, in soldiers using hash.

In 1974, Dr. Tenant told the Senate that cigarette smokers who get bronchitis and emphysema usually smoke ten or twenty years before their health problems arise. He stressed that these lung conditions are rarely seen in eighteen to twenty year old men. Dr. Tenant is certain that heavy hash smoking can cause lung problems much faster than cigarette use.

His observations become even more thought-provoking when you consider the fact that now good pot (like Colombian Gold or Sinsemilla) is at least as strong as most hash. For example, pure hash is about fifteen percent THC. Most American hash is only two percent THC. But good Gold can approach ten percent THC.

Part of Dr. Tenant's extensive testing included taking *biopsies* (samples of tissue) of the lining of the soldiers' breathing tubes. His research team found that the tissue changes in these young men looked more like what would be expected in older, long-time cigarette smokers. One of the soldiers had changes termed *squamous cell metaplasia*, a condition that frequently leads to lung cancer.

I. Read note E in the chapter "In Search of the Perfect Study."

Marijuana and the Brain

A. This study was criticized for several reasons. First, all of the subjects had regularly used at least one other drug. The test run (air encephalography) was not felt to be reliable. There were also questions about whether the control group was properly matched with the smokers in terms of age, previous drug use, and health.

B. Dr. Heath is the chairman of the Departments of Psychiatry and Neurology at Tulane University Medical School.

C. The deep brain areas researched by Dr. Heath are within the limbic region. This region surrounds the brain stem and contains structures (hypothalamus, septal region, hippocampus, amygdala) that have a broad impact on our lives. These areas figure centrally in pleasure, pain, fear, and human drives such as thirst, hunger, and sex. Additionally, this area involved the day-to-day functions of taste, smell, certain aspects of the nervous system, emotions, and alertness.

D. When Dr. Heath's work was first published, some people claimed his study's dope doses were too high. Dr. Heath has since published proof that the monkeys in his research received dope doses that compare equally with dope's effects on humans. He measured the levels of THC in the monkey's blood after the monkeys got stoned. By comparing these levels with those of human tokers, Dr. Heath developed a proper "monkey-size" joint. One tiny monkey reefer, when placed in the monkeys' smoking machine, equaled one joint for a person. (Remember, too, that Dr. Heath's comparison studies were done on government-grown dope of about 2.2 percent THC. Quality dope today is four to six percent THC, so a monkey joint may now equal only half a human joint.)

E. Until 1976, most researchers felt that EEGs of "heads" were not significantly different from EEGs of non-users. Numerous studies on chronic tokers (through the late 1970s) failed to identify clear evidence for lasting pot-related brain-wave changes.

However, in 1976 Dr. Robert Gilkeson (a psychiatrist from Cleveland, Ohio) began to re-examine the use of surface EEGs in the testing of marijuana users. By modifying the testing procedure to include tasking the subjects mentally, he found that dramatic differences can be found in the brain-waves of regular pot smokers. Dr. Gilkeson also claims that some previous studies *have* shown EEG changes in chronic smokers, although few of them have been published in key medical journals. He also feels that the method of reading the EEG "graph" is also important. (See note I in this section.)

F. The electron microscopic findings in the limbic area include
1. widened synaptic clefts (the space between nerve cells)
2. clumping of synaptic vesicles (considered a sign of old age in nerve cells)
3. deposits of dense, abnormal material in the synaptic clefts
4. broken, fragmented, and disorganized endoplasmic reticulum (the protein-producing machinery of the cell)

G. Dr. D. Harvey Powelson directed the Department of Psychiatry in the Student Health Service at the University of California at Berkeley from 1964 to 1972. He personally counseled 200 students a year, some of them several times a week for up to five years.

Initially, he assumed grass was harmless. But during his clinical experience, he changed his mind. He told the Senate that as a person continues regular (especially daily) use, he becomes less able to handle tasks where "judgment, memory, and logic are necessary" (reference 18, "Marijuana and the Brain").

H. Mitchell S. Rosenthal, president, Phoenix House Foundation, spoke before the Senate Subcommittee on Criminal Justice on the heatlh effects of marijuana (January 17, 1980). He voiced concern for the physical, mental, and emotional health of grass users. He opposed the decriminalization of grass. Though he acknowledged that there are many complex and delicate questions regarding fair penalties for various pot-related offenses, he felt that total removal of all penalties would create an unjustifiable atmosphere of official approval. He feels that decriminalization would "tell young Americans that pot is okay." He also cited the swift 1977 upswing in school-aged users (increase of 250,000) following decriminalization in New York State.

I. Dr. Gilkeson's study involves teenagers who have smoked at least three joints a week for four months. The abnormal brain waves he has identified occur when the patient is in the resting state as well as during mental activity.

While at rest, regular pot users tend to have far more brain rhythms of the theta speed (very slow) than non-users. Dr. Gilkeson says that "bursts" of theta activity (found in learning disabled people) are overlooked if the EEGs are machine scored, as is often the case. Machine scoring is one reason previous brain-wave studies haven't found much in the way of long-term marijuana effects. Another reason for the lack of EEG findings on dopers, according to Dr. Gilkeson, is that many researchers haven't known quite what to look for.

When Dr. Gilkeson's patients are tested in mental skills during the EEG exam, pot smokers show a weakened ability to switch into beta activity. (Normally, high frequency beta waves occur when a person focuses attention on one subject and when a person thinks quickly.) Instead of going into beta during a mental challenge, regular pot users tend to lag, showing slower alpha waves (slow waves) and more theta (very slow) waves than normal.

Dr. Gilkeson and his colleagues believe that how pot effects neurotransmitters (chemicals involved in relaying brain signals) is a key factor in the slowness of brain activity among regular grass users. In the future, he will be studying more about pot's ability to decrease either the production or release of seratonin, dopamine, and norepinephrine.

How About a Contact High?

A. As THC is slowly released from the body's storage (in fat) over a period of weeks, it eventually leaves the body through the urine and the feces (bowels). Approximately one-fourth of the THC a person takes in leaves through the urine. The rest leaves through the bowels (after THC is passed through the liver, into the gall bladder, then into the intestines as a part of the bile).

Dope and Driving

A. Information presented by Robert L. DuPont, M.D. at the Second Annual Conference on Marijuana, New York City, June 29, 1979 ("Marijuana Decriminalization: A Personal Reassessment").

B. In the airline pilot studies using a flight simulator, *major errors* were defined as mistakes that would (if committed during actual flight situations) cause the plane to get lost, run out of fuel, stall-out, or leave its designated altitude heading. *Minor errors* were defined as less serious deviations in altitude or heading.

Grass and Reproduction

A. Men and women have similar amounts of most hormones — except, obviously, the sex hormones. While both men and women have *testosterone* (male hormone) and *estrogen* (female hormone) in their bodies, men have much more testosterone than estrogen, and women have more estrogen. In addition, women's hormones vary or become more prominent during their monthly menstrual cycles and pregnancy.

B. As this book will show later, the concept of a *critical period* in a baby's development is important. During this time an unborn male develops the body parts and the chemical machinery to function as a normal adult male. In humans, a key period is during the third month of pregnancy. During this period, the child begins to produce increased testosterone, which is needed to "become" a boy. If testosterone is not produced, or if it is destroyed by an anti-testosterone drug taken by the mother, a boy will be born looking like a girl. It is believed that if less testosterone than normal is produced, the child may look perfectly normal but may have a less-than-normal sexual function when he matures. This concept is worth thinking about when you consider that THC reduces testosterone levels in male smokers. (See note N in this chapter.)

C. In a study at UCLA, thirteen healthy volunteers were tested for pot's effect on their hormones. Within two hours after smoking one joint, testosterone levels decreased in all thirteen subjects. The men's average testosterone value at three hours was 35 percent lower than before the men smoked.

D. In studies where men smoked pot daily for less than thirty days, their testosterone values were back to normal each morning of the study before smoking again. But in studies requiring men to smoke pot daily for more than thirty days, testosterone levels remain low. In the second month of such studies, morning levels prior to smoking are still depressed from the previous day's pot. This sustained drop may be because THC builds up in the testes (male glands producing testosterone); as daily smoking continues, the testes will contain increasing amounts of THC.

E. The Food and Drug Administration allows few drugs to be tested on women of childbearing age. Government policies against testing drugs on women became increasingly strict after the tragic use of thalidomide on European mothers during the 1960s. This tranquilizer caused physical defects in newborns. Presently, almost all legal drug testing in the United States is done on men.

F. In women, FSH controls the growth and maturation of the egg cell (follicle) that is released during each menstrual cycle. LH contributes to the release of the egg cell each month (ovulation) and maintains the structure that causes a monthly surge in progesterone.
   In men, FSH is needed for sperm to develop properly. LH controls the cells in the testes that produce testosterone.

G. The pattern of the drop of FSH and LH in mature female monkeys is almost identical to the drop of LH and testosterone in men. Human females of childbearing age have not been tested for grass's effects on their hormones. However, there has been some research on the hormones of post-menopausal women; these women, who are past childbearing age, show a drop in LH and FSH after smoking a joint.

H. In the studies on mature female monkeys, a joint's worth of THC dropped LH forty-four percent and FSH twenty-five percent. With five joints' worth, LH dropped sixty-eight percent below normal and FSH dropped fifty-six percent. The changes were measured at six hours following the THC dose. With five joints' worth of THC, the hormones were still low at twelve and twenty-four hours, while one joint's worth only caused a decrease at six hours.

I. In these same studies on mature female monkeys, Dr. Carol Smith studied the part of the menstrual cycle called the *luteal phase* (the period in the middle of the cycle, after the egg is released). Dr. Smith found that THC caused a hormone disruption in the cycle (low levels of LH early in the next cycle, low levels of progesterone late in the next cycle.) These effects are accompanied by a failure of the egg to be released. This work demonstrates that THC interferes with the portion of the menstrual cycle that is the most vital in the ability to conceive children.

J. According to Dr. Robert Kolodny of the Masters and Johnson Institute in St. Louis, several doctors have reported that irregular periods occur more often in pot-smoking patients. Although there are not published studies that offer proof, the hormone imbalances caused by grass would seem to make irregular periods more likely. Actual proof of this question would require extensive survey tests.

K. The study on sperm counts used five paid volunteers (ages twenty to twenty-seven) who had smoked at least three to five joints per week in the last few years. At the start of the study, they were told not to smoke dope for three weeks (to establish their normal sperm counts). They then worked up to eight joints a day. After that, they smoked at least ten doobies a day for three weeks. After four weeks of heavy burning, their sperm counts decreased at least thirty percent and as much as seventy percent in one man. The average drop in total sperm per sample was fifty-eight percent below the men's starting values (before smoking).
   A recent study by the same research team tested sixteen more smokers in the manner just described (*Marihuana: Biological Effects*, Pergamon Press, 1979, pp. 429-439). At the end of four weeks of heavy smoking, the subjects' sperm counts dropped significantly, their sperm cells moved slower than normal, and they had an increased number of abnormal sperm cells.

L. The normal range of male testosterone levels is pretty wide. Accordingly, many men who have their testosterone levels cut by one-third will still be in the range of "normal." That is, an average man can lose a lot of testosterone from grass and still have more than another man on the low end of normal. For this reason, some people claim that heavy pot smoking doesn't cause *abnormally* low testosterone levels (in most men).

But this view really misses the point. When a person's hormone levels drop because of a drug, I believe it is definitely abnormal *for that person.* When a person's body chemistry goes downhill, it doesn't have to roll past the lowest person on the hill before something has gone wrong.

M. Several research teams have found that infants' brains are extra-sensitive to THC. In a recent study, brain cells from three-day old rats were affected more by THC than brain cells from rats of any other age; THC caused less protein and DNA materials to be produced in the younger rats. This finding is not surprising when you consider that the young developing brain, both in lab animals and humans, is extremely rich in fat — therefore, it's a THC magnet.

N. The pregnant mice were exposed to THC during the last day of pregnancy (THC is transferred to the fetus) and for six days following birth (THC is transferred through the breast milk). Another marijuana chemical, cannabinol (CBN), also decreased adult male sexual function in this experiment. The ability of chemicals other than THC to cause physical problems helps to illustrate the complexity of studying marijuane. Far more than THC is involved.

It is believed that THC has both direct and indirect effects on testosterone. THC accumulates in the testes and directly lowers testosterone production. It also acts on the hypothalamic-pituitary axis to lower testosterone in an indirect manner.

O. The babies who survived birth to mothers given THC acted differently from monkeys unexposed to THC. According to Dr. Ethyl Sassenrath, the THC monkeys seemed to lack the proper "brakes" when they played — they played too rough for the other monkeys.

The THC babies also showed some learning difficulties, having a shorter attention span and a more difficult time remembering what they saw. These problems in behavior and learning are clues that some brain damage is present in the monkeys born to stoned mothers.

P. In children born to mothers who used alcohol during pregnancy, there are more problems with mental retardation, heart disease and a variety of other growth defects, than among the general population. The *Fetal Alcohol Syndrome* is the term given to these alcohol-related problems.

Grass, Genes, and Chromosomes

A. The shape of chromosomes is actually a double-helix. Not quite crisscross-shaped, chromosomes pair up during cell divison to create a spiral-shaped ladder. In case you are wondering, the silly-looking man in the picture (Mr. Chromosome) has "chromosome-shaped" legs!

B. The occurrence of "lost chromosomes" in heavy grass use is a result of cells not dividing properly. When a cell divides normally (into two new cells), exactly half the chromosomes go into one cell, and half go to the other cell. When something goes wrong in division (called *segregational errors of chromosomes*, or SEC), one cell ends up with too many chromosomes, and the other new cell gets too few. Lost chromosomes are probably a result of THC's effect on the stage of cell division called *metaphase*.

C. Cancer is commonly associated with tumors (tissue masses made up of cancer cells). Cancer also describes a series of changes where normal cells take on patterns of growth and appearance that are increasingly abnormal and out of control. The research team headed by Dr. Leuchtenberger has proven in several experiments that marijuana smoke causes cancerous changes in lung cells. These changes include increased size of nuclei and nucleoli, abnormally shaped cells, strange chromosome patterns, and rapid and abnormal growth of cells. The appearance of the lung cells also changed, from normal (epithelial) cells to cells best described as scar tissue cells, or "gristle" cells (fibroblasts).

D. The variety of cancer found in Dr. Szepsenwol's mice was fibrosarcoma. The mice were given THC (in sesame oil as a solvent). The control mice received just sesame oil. The weekly treatments were given from six months to slightly over a year.

E. A *drumstick nucleus* describes a portion of the nuclear membrane that has a noticeable shape when viewed under a microscope. In females, the membranes of cell nuclei (plural of *nucleus*) have the drumstick appearance. Men normally lack drumsticks.

F. Dr. Akira Morishima of Columbia University gave the mice daily THC doses equal to two joints a day. He presented his research at the Second Annual Conference on Marijuana in New York City on June 29, 1979.

G. The daily doses of THC given to the mice were five and ten milligrams per kilogram of body weight. If a 150-pound human burned THC at the same rate as a 150-pound mouse, these doses would figure out to be over ten and twenty joints per day of good pot for a person. But mice burn dope (and most all drugs) about *ten times as fast* as a person. Therefore, these doses were equal to about two joints a day for a person. The way scientists figure out how much dope a mouse or rat needs to equal a joint for a person is discussed in the section "In Search of the Perfect Study."

In this same study on mouse sperm cells, several marijuana chemicals besides THC were tested. Cannabinol (CBN) and cannabidiol (CBD), which do not give a high, also caused a high number of abnormal sperm cells. This test shows the powerful affect that marijuana chemicals other than the commonly studied THC can have on the body.

The testing of chemicals for their ability to cause abnormal sperm in mice is considered a good, rough screening test for mutagens, which are chemicals able to cause *mutations* (permanent changes in cells). About two-thirds of all chemicals that are mutagens can be discovered by the mouse sperm test. (Mutagens usually cause cancer, as well as mutations.) Therefore, the ability of THC to cause abnormal sperm (in mice) at doses that compare to daily smoking in humans is another hint that grass can mess up the genetic machinery.

Marijuana and Immunity

A. The body's second type of defense system is called the *humoral immunity system*. This system is composed of cells that travel in the blood and produce antibodies, chemicals that fight poisons and bacteria. Pot affects this system less than it does the cell-mediated system.

B. The ability of lymphocytes (defense cells) to react to foreign red blood cells (like cells from sheep or guinea pigs) is probably weaker in heavy tokers. However, the "foreign invader" test is run in a test tube, and thus it is difficult to draw conclusions about the disease-preventing ability of dopers.

C. Skin tests are a more direct test of the immune system. In the tests run thus far, dopers do about as well as nonsmokers. This test obviously doesn't tell the whole story, however, as even a diseased immune system will form a skin reaction to foreign chemicals. (The common TB test given to school children would be an example of a skin test.)

D. Lab animals given THC require longer for their bodies to destroy foreign skin grafts. Skin grafts are a test of the cell-mediated defense system.

E. People with weakened immune systems get cancer more easily. For example, kidney transplant patients are given drugs to weaken their immune systems (so they don't destroy their new kidney). Kidney transplant patients are eighty times more likely to get cancer than the general population.

F. See note G in "Marijuana and the lungs."

Can You Get Hooked?

A. The most important body organ in development of tolerance to any drug is the liver. The liver, a factory that builds and takes apart countless chemicals, deactivates most of the drugs the body takes in. When the liver cells get geared up for a particular drug, the drug gets torn apart much faster. Thus, a heroin junkie can burn up heroin much faster than a beginner. The same goes for alcoholics and experienced users of most drugs.

Tolerance also develops in another way. Not only does the body burn a particular drug faster, but the individual cells in the body also get used to it; tired of it, you might say. That's why experienced hash heads need several times as much THC to get stoned as beginning tokers. The brain cells of long-time heavy users come to view THC as old stuff — more THC is needed to get them drugged.

B. The thirty-day tolerance study used THC given in capsule form. The amount given was referred to as "ten joints per day," based on each joint having twenty milligrams of THC. Since today's joint contains about forty milligrams of THC, the subjects in this test received a present-day dose of five joints per day. The subjects received thirty milligram capsules at 8 A.M., noon, 6 P.M., 9 P.M., and 4 A.M., with a double dose at bedtime.

C. A twenty-one-day test of twenty-eight men was run by Harvard University. The subjects smoked an average of four joints a day. As the test progressed, tolerance effects were shown by heart rates. The rapid heartbeat caused by grass returned to normal faster at the end of the test, when tolerance had built up. Smokers also rated themselves as less high from the same amount of dope toward the end of the test.

A ninety-four-day study by UCLA showed that bronchial tubes dilated less at the end of the study, indicating short-term tolerance.

D. The withdrawal symptoms described were observed in the thirty-day test mentioned earlier in the chapter. Dr. Reese Jones and Dr. Neil Benowitz (University of California, San Francisco) titled the study "The 30-Day Trip." In their published account of the experiment, they made the following statement about whether a person can become dependent on marijuana:

> If one defines dependence as an altered biological state associated with the consumption of a drug so that its use must be continued to prevent the development of specific signs and symptoms on withdrawal then the patients gave evidence of developing physical dependence. (*Pharmacology of Marihuana*, Raven Press, 1976, p. 627.)

E. If naloxone is given to a human heroin addict, withdrawal symptoms will begin almost immediately. A heroin addict requires heroin constantly in the blood to avoid going into withdrawal. Naloxone inactivates heroin (plus morphine, opium, and other narcotics) in the blood, so the person's body doesn't feel any heroin when naloxone is given; therefore without heroin, the person goes into withdrawal. This process is exactly when happened in one study when rats used to high, daily doses of THC were given naloxone. Like the heroin addicts, the rats went into instant THC withdrawal.

F. Marijuana doesn't cause a violent physical withdrawal, but that fact doesn't prove it isn't addicting. A violent withdrawal is more likely to occur when a regularly used drug is suddenly cut off. In the case of THC, even if a regular user goes cold turkey, THC still gets "leaked" back into the blood stream (from storage in fat). It is possible that the small amounts of THC still present in the blood after a toker goes cold turkey might reduce possible withdrawal effects. Tests with naloxone on human pot smokers would probably shed light on this subject.

The editor of a recent volume on grass uses just one sentence to summarize the evidence about whether grass is addictive. In *Marihuana: Biological Effects* (a highly technical research volume), Dr. W.D.M. Paton says: "Cannabis [marijuana] satisfies the usual criteria for an addictive drug."

G. Caffeine is an addicting drug that often produces headaches as a withdrawal symptom. An average cup of coffee has eighty-five milligrams of caffeine. An average cup of tea has fifty milligrams of caffeine. A can of cola has about forty-eight milligrams of caffeine. Half of the caffeine in colas come from the kola nut; the other half is added to give the drinks an extra "buzz."

When a child drinks a can of cola (any brand), the kid gets more of a buzz than an adult who drinks a cup of coffee. That's because children weigh less.

An average eight year old who drinks two cans of cola in a day gets a high (from caffeine) equal to an adult who drinks three cups of coffee or five cups of tea. If the eight year old drinks a whole sixteen ounce cola, he or she gets a speed buzz equal to two cups of coffee. I wonder how many children who can't sit still in school or at home are actually "wired-out" on caffeine? How many young people are trained for later drug use by an early introduction to caffeine?

H. On the bottle labels of colas, when you get past the large amounts of sugar and caffeine, you come to a long list of artificial colors, flavors, preservatives, and other goodies that help make a multi-billion dollar industry out of chemical grogs with absolutely no useful nutritional value.

I. The National Center for Disease Control estimates that alcohol abuse costs the nation over forty billion dollars a year (from medical care, auto accidents, violent crimes, social programs, fire losses, and lost work). They estimate that alcohol killed over 30,000 people from liver disease in 1976.

J. Representatives from the Food and Drug Administration recently reported studies linking caffeine with an increase in birth defects (Newhouse News Service, Feb. 26, 1980). Dr. Thomas Collins of the FDA suggests that beverages with caffeine are not as safe as people have previously believed. Dr. Collins says that written warnings on colas, coffee, and tea may be suggested in the future.

K. In 1979, 91.6 pounds of sugar added to foods was consumed for every man, woman and child in America. This was down a bit from a record 101.8 pounds *per capita* in 1970.

In Search of the Perfect Study

A. Figuring out how much grass or THC given to a rat, mouse, or monkey equals a joint for a person, is rather complicated. However, scientists have developed conversion factors that help calculate dope doses for lab animals. These conversion factors show how many times faster lab animals burn up drugs than humans.

For example, the most commonly accepted conversion factor for a mouse is twelve. This means that if you had a big mouse that weighed as much as a person, that mouse would have to smoke twelve joints to get as high as a person who smoked one joint. For rats, the conversion factor is around seven; for monkeys, it's around three.

This concept is important in relating lab test results to people's everyday lives. People who don't understand conversion factors often think the doses of THC used on rats or mice is far too high. Take, for example, a mouse that actually received four "human joints" of THC per day. Someone who didn't understand conversion factors would claim the mouse received almost fifty joints a day (4×12).

B. Scientists measure the strength of pot in milligrams of THC (about 28,000 milligrams equal an ounce). Five to ten milligrams of THC is usually enough to give a good buzz.

An average joint now contains thirty or forty milligrams of THC. Most of the studies in this book that mention numbers of joints refer to the old government figure of twenty milligrams of THC per joint. Since a joint of good pot now contains twice that amount, you could really go through this book and cut the number of joints in half (where experiments are given in numbers of joints per day). In other words, many of the experiments on grass's health effects *underestimate* the effects. (People today smoke just as many joints as several years ago, only today's dope is much stronger.)

C. The editor of *Marihuana: Biological Effects*, Dr. W.D.M. Paton, used a French term to describe dope's ability to cause physical damage to the user. The term, *inconstestablement nocif*, means damage or harm beyond a doubt. Dr. Paton, the director of the British drug research program and a professor at Oxford University in England, is also considered by his colleagues to be one of the world's leading pharmacologists (experts on drugs).

D. In the Jamaica study, the ganja smokers had lower amounts of oxygen in their blood (pO_2 values). In addition, five times as many smokers had high values for *packed cell volume* (PCV), a measure of red cells in the blood. Red blood cells carry oxygen, and their numbers tend to increase when the body doesn't get enough oxygen. This situation often occurs in cigarette smokers (their lungs don't work as well, their bodies are "starved" for oxygen, so they produce more red cells). The blood tests of the Jamaican tokers suggest their lungs worked even less well than the "nonsmokers" (remember, of these, two-thirds were cigarette smokers).

E. Before x-rays accurately show marijuana-related damage, most people will have wheezing and chronic coughing. Tests such as comprehensive spirometry (breathing ability), radioisotopic scanning, and bronchial biopsies will detect any damage much earlier than x-rays.

F. Read *Lost chromosomes and marijuana* in the chapter "Grass, Genes, and Chromosomes."

Making Use of the Facts

A. The effect of marijuana on epileptic seizures is complicated by the fact that different marijuana chemicals have very different effects. Several of the cannabinoids, mainly CBD and CBN, have been studied as having *anticonvulsant* activity (they tend to reduce the likelihood of seizures in epileptics). These drugs may someday be of some value in medical treatment.

However, THC (delta-9-THC, the main drug for a high) has a tendency to cause seizures in epileptic laboratory animals. Marijuana-induced seizures have also been reported for a human epileptic. ("Cannabis and Epilepsy," R. Karler and S. A. Turkanis, in *Marihuana: Biological effects* [G. G. Nahas and W.D.M. Paton, ed.], Pergamon Press, Oxford and New York, pp. 619-657, 1979).

Thus it appears that smoking pot may *increase* the chance of seizures in epileptics, even though several cannabinoids tends to reduce the risk.

B. The immediate effects of marijuana on a healthy user often include an increase in heart rate (tachycardia). Not much is known about the long-term effects of grass on the heart.

Most healthy tokers tolerate the slight strain pot puts on the heart without much trouble. However, people with some degree of heart trouble may experience chest pains (angina pectoris) when smoking a joint. The American Medical Association reports that a joint can probably trigger heart pains more rapidly than cigarettes. (*Marihuana and Health*, Seventh Annual Report to the U. S. Congress, pp. 18-19, 1977).

Passing the Word

A. The 1963 date of "proof" of the cigarette-cancer and heart disease link refers to the 1963 report by the U. S. Surgeon General's Special Committee on Tobacco and Health.

What's Normal for NORML?

A. The National Commission on Marijuana called people who used pot once a month or less (*experimental users*). *Intermittent users* are people who got high two to ten times a month. This quote used by NORML evades the Commission's findings on 4,500,000 *moderate users* (smoking eleven times a month to once daily) and 500,000 *heavy users* (smoking several times daily). The National Commission noted that heavy users tend to become alienated from society, have a reduced concern for personal well-being, and display emotional immaturity. They are generally more pessimistic, insecure, and irresponsible (pages 38 and 62 of the report). An interesting review of the report is found in the *Bulletin of the New York Academy of Medicine*, vol. 50, no. 1, pp. 55-75, January 1974 ("The First Report of the National Commission on Marihuana — 1972: Signal of Misunderstanding or Exercise in Ambiguity," by G. G. Nahas and A. Greenwood).

B. This quote is meaningless in 1979. Consider these facts: Most of the medical hazards of pot that are now well known were not understood in 1972; The number of people smoking pot has increased considerably since 1972 (it has more than doubled among junior high and high school ages.); The street pot now sold is over three times as strong as in 1972.

C. Government studies show that thousands of traffic deaths are statistically accountable to marijuana use. This book has also discussed numerous examples of physical damage and disturbances of bodily processes that result from smoking grass.

D. The chapter "Grass, Genes, and Chromosomes" mentions evidence on genetic defects that was not available in 1972. While this issue is far from settled, marijuana seems to cause problems in cell division, which results in cells that have too few chromosomes. In addition, the government's decision to forbid testing marijuana on women is based on the threat of genetic damage to women's egg cells.

E. In "Marijuana and the Brain," we discussed the growing evidence that says grass can cause brain damage (the work of Dr. Heath and Dr. Gilkeson, for instance). In 1972, marijuana research was just getting started, while alcohol's relationship to brain damage was already well known. Many clues (such as the fact that THC builds up in the brain tissue) point to marijuana as an even greater threat to brain health than alcohol.

F. Since 1972, the tolerance effect to grass has been well established in humans. The chapter "Can You Get Hooked" cites studies that indicate a strong possibility of physical dependence resulting from sustained use of marijuana. The concluding sentence in the summary of *Marihuana: Biological Effects* (Nahas, G.G. and Paton, W.D.M., eds., Pergamon Press; Oxford, New York, p. 738, 1979) reads: "Cannabis [pot] satisfies the usual criteria for an addictive drug."

G. I discussed NORML's brochure with Dr. Brill on Feb. 26, 1980. He said he believes very strongly that NORML has misrepresented the message of the National Commission's Report ever since it was published. His comments before the Senate in 1974 emphasize the fact that the Commission's report never gave pot a clean bill of health. Dr. Brill also gave permission to print his opinion that NORML's pamphlet gives a distorted view of the current medical understanding of marijuana and completely ignores the massive evidence that grass is medically harmful.

H. "Reprinted from *U,S, News & World Report*. Copyright 1978 U.S. News & World Report, Inc."

I. Dr. DuPont gave a formal statement of his views on decriminalization at the Second Annual Conference on Marijuana (New York University, June 29, 1979). In his paper, he stated that completely removing all penalties for pot use gives the message that it is "okay" to smoke pot. He feels that the "okay" message is foolish in light of the new evidence on serious health hazards and the trend toward increased use of grass (especially by junior high and high schoolers). I spoke with Dr. DuPont on Feb. 1, 1980, and he said that when he made the 1975 statement that NORML used in its "Fact" leaflet, he never meant that pot was harmless; rather that we needed a greater effort to try and reduce alcohol and tobacco use. Dr. DuPont now believes that marijuana presents a greater problem to America than either alcohol or tobacco.

J. NORML's "Official Policy" brochure is a collection of statements adopted by its board of directors on November 30, 1978.

References

It's a Matter of Chemistry

1. Lemberger, L., Silberstein, S.D., Axelrod, J., and Kopin, I.J. Marijuana: Studies on the disposition and metabolism of delta-9-tetrahydrocannabinol in man. *Science* **170**: 1320 (1970).
2. Graham, J.D.P. *Cannabis and health.* New York: Academic Press (1976). pp. 77-107.
3. Nahas, G.G. Biomedical aspects of cannabis usage. *Bulletin on Narcotics* **XXIX** (2): 13-27 (1977).
4. Gill, W.E., and Jones, G. Brain levels of delta-1-tetrahydrocannabinol and its metabolites in mice. *Biochemical Pharmacology* **21**: 2237 (1972).
5. Garrett, E.R., and Hunt, C.A. Physiochemical properties, solubility, and protein binding of delta-9-THC. *Journal of Pharmaceutical Sciences* **63**: 1056 (1974).
6. Mantilla-Plata, B., and Harbison, R.D. distribution studies of C delta-9-THC in mice: Effect of vehicle, route of administration, and duration of treatment. *Toxicology and Applied Pharmacology*, **34**: 292-300 (1975).
7. Kreuz, D.S., and Axelrod, J. Delta-9-tetrahydrocannabinol: Localization in body fat. *Science* **179**: 391-392 (1973).
8. Carchman, R.A., et al. Marihuana and cell function. In *Marihuana: Biological effects* (Nahas, G.G., and Paton, W.D.M., eds.). Oxford: Pergamon Press (1979), pp, 219-228.
9. Garrett, E.R. Pharmacokinetics and disposition of delta-9-tetrahydrocannabinol and its metabolites. In *Marihuana: Biological effects* (Nahas, G.G., and Paton, W.D.M., eds.). Oxford: Pergamon Press (1979), pp. 105-121.
10. Hattori, T., Jakubovic, A., and McGeer, P.L. The effect of cannabinoids on the number of nuclear membrane-attached ribosomes in infant rat brain. *Neuropharmacology* **12**: 995 (1973).
11. Huot, J. Cellular and biochemical alterations induced in vitro by delta-1-THC: Effects on cell proliferation, nucleic acids, plasma cell membrane ATPase, and adenylate cyclase. In *Marihuana: Chemistry, biochemistry, and cellular effects* (Nahas, G.G., et al., eds.). New York: Springer-Verlag (1976), pp. 313-327.
12. Blevins, R.D., and Regan, J.D. Delta-9-tetrahydrocannabinol: Effect on macromolecular synthesis in human and mammalian cells. *Archives of Toxicology* **35**: 127-135 (1976).
13. DeSoize, B., et al. Inhibition of human lymphocyte transformation in vitro by natural cannabinoids and olivetol. *Federation Proceedings* **34**: 783 (1975).
14. Jakubovic, A., and McGeer, P.L. In vitro inhibition of protein and nucleic acid synthesis in rat testicular tissue by cannabis. In *Marihuana: Chemistry, biochemistry, and cellular effects* (Nahas, G.G., et al., eds.). New York: Springer-Verlag (1976), 223-241.
15. Morishima, A., et al. Effects of marijuana smoking, cannabinoids and olivetol on replication of human lymphocytes: Formation of micronucleic. In *Pharmacology of Marihuana* (Braude, M.D., and Szara, S., eds.). New York: Raven Press (1976), pp. 711-722.
16. Leuchtenberger, C., et al. Effects of marijuana and tobacco smoke on DNA and chromosomal complement in lung explants. *Nature* **242**: 403-404 (1973).

17. Morishima, A., Henrich, R.T., Jayaraman, J., and Nahas, G.G. Haploid metaphases in cultured lymphocytes of marijuana smokers. In *Marihuana: Biological effects* (Nahas, G.G., and Paton, W.D.M., eds.), Oxford: Pergamon Press (1979), pp. 371-376.
18. Zimmerman, A.M., Zimmerman, S., and Raj, A.Y. Effects of cannabinoids on spermatogenesis in mice. In *Marihuana: Biological effects* (Nahas, G.G., and Paton, W.D.M., eds.), Oxford: Pergamon Press (1979), pp. 407-418.
19. Leuchtenberger, C., and Leuchtenberger, R. Correlated cytological and cytochemical studies of the effects of fresh smoke from marijuana cigarettes on growth and DNA metabolism of animal and human lung cultures. In *Pharmacology of Marihuana* (Braude, M.C., and Szara, S., eds.). New York: Raven Press (1976), pp. 595-612.

Marijuana and the Brain

1. Campbell, A.M.G., et al. Cerebral atrophy in young cannabis smokers. *Lancet* **2** (7736): 1219-1224 (1971).
2. Co, B.T., Goodwin, D.W., et al. Absence of cerebral atrophy in chronic cannabis users. *Journal of the American Medical Association* **237**: 1231-1232 (1977).
3. Kuehnle, J., et al. Computerized tomographic examination of heavy marihuana smokers. *Journal of the American Medical Association* **237**: 1229-1230 (1977).
4. Marihuana-Hashish Epidemic and its Impact on United States Security. Hearings before the Subcommittee to investigate the Administration of the Internal Security Act and Other Internal Security Laws of the Committee on the Judiciary, United States Senate. Ninety-third Congress, Second Session. U.S. Government Printing Office, Washington, D.C. (1974).
5. Axelrod, J. Testimony before the Senate Subcommittee on Internal Security. May 1974, ref. 4, pp. 142-146 (1974).
6. Heath, R.G., et al. Cannabis sativa: Effects on brain function and ultrastructure in rhesus monkeys. *Biological Psychiatry* **15**: 657-690 (1980).
7. Heath, R.G. Testimony before the Senate Subcommittee on Internal Security. May 1974, ref. 4, pp. 50-70 (1974).
8. McIsaac, W.M., et al. Distribution of marihuana in monkey brain and concomitant behavioral effects. *Nature* **230**: 593-594 (1971).
9. Izquierdo, I., et al. Effect of cannabidiol and of other cannabis sativa compounds on hippocampal seizure discharges. *Psychopharmacologia* **28**: 95-102 (1973).
10. Fehr, K.O., Kalant, H., and Knox, G.V. Residual effects of high-dose cannabis treatment on learning, muricidal behavior and neurophysiological correlates in rats. In *Marihuana: Biological effects* (Nahas, G.G., and Paton, W.D.M., eds.). Oxford: Pergamon Press (1979), pp. 681-691.
11. Heath, R.G., et al. Chronic marihuana smoking: Its effect on function and structure of the primate brain. In *Marihuana: Biological effects* (Nahas, G.G., and Paton, W.D.M., eds.). Oxford: Pergamon Press (1979), pp. 713-730.
12. Myers, W.A., and Heath, R.G. Cannabis sativa: Ultrastructural changes in organelles of neurons in brain septal region of monkeys. *Journal of Neuroscience Research* **4**: 9-17 (1979).
13. McGeer, P.L., and Jakubovic, A. Ultrastructural and biochemical changes in CNS induced by marihuana. In *Marihuana: Biological effects* (Nahas, G.G., and Paton, W.D.M., eds.). Oxford: Pergamon Press (1979), pp. 519-530.
14. Luthra, Y.K. Brain biochemical alterations in neonates of dams treated orally with delta-9-THC during gestation and lactation. In *Marihuana: Biological effects* (Nahas, G.G., and Paton, W.D.M., eds.). Oxford: Pergamon Press (1979), pp. 531-537.
15. Kennedy, J.S., and Waddell, W.J. Whole body autoradiography of the pregnant mouse after administration of 14-C-delta-9-THC. *Toxicology and Applied Pharmacology* **22**: 252-258 (1972).
16. Vardaris, R.M., et al. Chronic administration of delta-9-THC to pregnant rats: Studies of pup behavior and placental transfer. *Pharmacology, Biochemistry, and Behavior* **4**: 249-254 (1976).

17. Powelson, D.H. Marijuana: More dangerous than you know. *Reader's Digest,* December 1974, pp. 95-99 (1974).
18. Powelson, D.H. Testimony before the Senate Subcommittee on Internal Security. May 1974, ref. 4, pp. 18-29 (1974).
19. Kolansky, H., and Moore, W.T. Effects of marihuana on adolescents and young adults. *Journal of the American Medical Association* **216:** 486-492 (1971).
20. Kolansky, H., and Moore, W.T. Toxic effects of chronic marihuana use. *Journal of the American Medical Association* **222:** 35-41 (1972).
21. Schwarz, C.J. Testimony before the Senate Subcommittee on Internal Security. May 1974, ref. 4, pp. 200-206 (1974).
22. Zeidenberg, P. Testimony before the Senate Subcommittee on Internal Security. May 1974, ref. 4, pp. 189-197 (1974).
23. Moore, W.T. Testimony before the Senate Subcommittee on Internal Security. May 1974, ref. 4, pp. 154-169 (1974).
24. Hart, R.H. A psychiatric classification of cannabis intoxication. *Journal of the American Academy of Psychiatry and Neurology* **1** (4): 83-97 (1976).
25. Rubin, W., and Comitas, L. *Ganja in Jamaica: A medical anthropological study of chronic cannabis use.* Mouton Press, The Hauge (1975).
26. Coggins, W.J. Costa Rica cannabis project. An interim report on the medical aspects. In *Pharmacology of Marihuana* (Braude, M.C. and Szara, S., eds.). New York: Raven Press, (1976) pp. 667-670.
27. Soueif, M.I. Differential Association between chronic use and brain function defects. *Annals of the New York Academy of Sciences* **282:** 323-343 (1976).
28. Stefanis, C., et al. Psychophysiologic effects of acute cannabis smoking in long-term users. *Annals of the New York Academy of Sciences* **282:** 375-386 (1976).
29. Wig, N.N. and Varma, V.K. Patterns of long-term heavy cannabis use in north India and its effects on cognitive functions: A preliminary report. Drug and Alcohol Dependence **2:** 211-219 (1977).
30. Radouco-Thomas, S., et al. Pharmacogenetic studies in cannabis and narcotics effects of delta-1-THC and morphine in developing rats. In *Marihuana: Chemistry, biochemistry and cellular Effects* (Nahas, G.G., et al. eds.). New York: Springer-Verlag (1976), pp. 481-494.

Marijuana and the Lungs

1. Tashkin, D.P., et al. Chronic effects of heavy marihuana smoking on pulmonary function in healthy young males. In *The Pharmacology of Marihuana* (Braude, M.C., and Szara, S., eds.). New York: Raven Press (1976), pp. 291-295.
2. Fleischman, R.W., Baker, J.R., and Rosenkrantz, H. Pulmonary pathologic changes in rats exposed to marihuana smoke for 1 year. *Toxicology and Applied Pharmacology* **47:** 557-566 (1979).
3. Novotny, M., et al. A possible chemical basis for the higher mutagenicity of marijuana smoke as compared with tobacco smoke. *Experentia* **32:** 280-282 (1976).
4. Peterson, R.C. Importance of inhalation patterns in determining effects of marihuana use. *The Lancet,* March 31, 727-728 (1979).
5. Baker, J.R., and Rosenkrantz, H. A simple method for demonstrating tetrahydrocannabinols in fresh or fixed frozen sections. *Journal of Histochemistry and Cytochemistry* **20:** 827-832 (1972).
6. Freudenthal, R.I., et al. Distribution of delta-9-THC in the mouse. *British Journal of Pharmacology* **44:** 244-249 (1972).
7. Huber, G.L., et al. An experimental animal model for quantifying the biologic effects of marijuana on the defense system of the lung. In *Marihuana: Biological effects* (Nahas, G.G., and Paton, W.D.M., eds.). Oxford: Pergamon Press (1979), pp. 301-328.
8. Leuchtenberger, C., and Leuchtenberger, R. Cytological and cytochemical studies of the effects of fresh marihuana cigarette smoke on growth and DNA metabolism

of animal and human lung cultures. In *The Pharmacology of Marihuana* (Braude, M.C., and Szara, S., eds.). New York: Raven Press (1976), pp. 595-612.

9. Henderson, R.L., et al. Respiratory manifestations of hashish smoking. *Archives of Otolaryngology* **95**: 248-251 (1972).
10. Tennant, F.S., et al. Medical manifestations associated with hashish. *Journal of the American Medical Association* **216**: 1965-1969 (1971).
11. Rubin, V., and Comitas, L. *Ganja in Jamaica: A medical anthropological study of chronic marihuana use*. Mouton Press, The Hague (1975).

What about a Contact High?

1. Zeidenberg, P., Bourdon, R., and Nahas, G.G. Marijuana intoxication by passive inhalation: Documentation by detection of urinary metabolites. *American Journal of Psychiatry* **134**: 76-77 (1977).
2. Bourdon, R. Identification and quantitation of cannabinoids in urine by gallium chelate formation. In *Marihuana: Chemistry, biochemistry, and cellular effects* (Nahas, G.G., eds.). New York: Springer-Verlag (1976).
3. Rubenstein, K.E. Determination of cannabinoids in urine by EMIT homogeneous enzyme immunoassay. In *Marihuana: Biological effects* (Nahas, G.G., and Paton, W.D.M., eds.). Oxford: Pergamon Press (1979), pp. 89-99.

Dope and Driving

1. Petersen, R.C. Complex psychomotor performance in driving and flying. In *Marihuana and health - Sixth annual report to the U.S. Congress from the Secretary of Health, Education, and Welfare*. Washington, D.C.: U.S. Goverment Printing Office (1976), pp. 23-24.
2. Janowsky, D.S., et al. Marijuana effects on simulated flying ability. *American Journal of Psychiatry* **133** (4): 384-388 (1976).
3. Meacham, M.P. et al. Effects of marihuana on flying ability. *Journal of the American Medical Association* **230** (9): 1258 (1974).
4. Blaine, J.D., et al. Marihuana smoking and simulated flying performance. In *Pharmacology of Marihuana* (Braude, M.C., and Szara, S., eds.). New York: Raven Press (1976), pp. 445-447.
5. Tinklenberg, J.R., et al. Marihuana and alcohol: Time production and memory functions. *Archives of General Psychiatry* **27**: 812-815 (1972).
6. Jones, R.T., and Stone, G.R. Psychological studies of marijuana and alcohol in man. *Psychopharmacologia* **18**: 108-117 (1970).

Grass and Reproduction

1. Kolodny, R.C., et al. Depression of plasma testosterone and acute marihuana administration. In *Pharmacology of Marihuana* (Braude, M.C., and Szara, S., eds.). New York: Raven Press (1976), pp. 217-225.
2. Cohen, S. The 94-day cannabis study. *Annals of the New York Academy of Sciences* **282**: 211-220 (1976).
3. Kolodny, R.C. Paper presented at the International Academy of Sex Research, St. Louis, Missouri (1975).
4. Smith, C.G., et al. Effect of delta-9-THC on female reproductive function. In *Marihuana: Biological effects* (Nahas, G.G., and Paton, W.D.M., eds.). Oxford: Pergamon Press (1979), pp. 449-467.

5. Hembree, W.D., et al. Marihuana's effects on human gonadal function. In *Marihuana: Chemistry, biochemistry, and cellular effects* (Nahas, G.G. eds.). New York: Springer-Verlag (1976), pp. 521-532.
6. Harbison, R.D. Maternal Distribution and Placental Transfer of C-delta-9-THC in Pregnant Mice. *Toxicology and Applied Pharmacology*, **19**, 413-414 (1971).
7. Vardaris, R.M., et al. Chronic administration of delta-9-THC to pregnant rats: Studies of pup behavior and placental transfer. *Pharmacology, Biochemistry, and Behavior* **4**, 249-254 (1976).
8. McGeer, P.L. and Jakubovic, A. Ultrastructural and biochemical changes in CNS induced by marihuana. In *Marihuana: Biological effects* (Nahas, G.G., and Paton, W.D.M. eds.). Oxford: Pergamon Press (1979), pp. 519-530.
9. Jabubovic, A., et al. Excretion of THC and its metabolites in ewes' milk. *Toxicology and Applied Pharmacology* **28**, 38-43 (1974).
10. Bloch, E., et al. Effects of cannabinoids on reproduction and development. *Vitamins and Hormones* **36**: 203-258 (1979).
11. Cozens, D.D., et al. The effect of a crude marihuana extract on embryonic and foetal development of the rabbit. In *Marihuana: Biological effects* (Nahas, G.G., and Paton, W.D.M., eds.). Oxford: Pergamon Press (1979), pp. 469-477.
12. Mantilla-Plata, B., et al. Delta-9-THC-induced changes in prenatal growth and development of mice. *Toxicology and Applied Pharmacology* **33**, 333-340 (1975).
13. Joneja, M.G. A study of teratologic effects of intravenous, subcutaneous and intragastric administration of delta-9-THC in mice. *Toxicology and Applied Pharmacology* **36**, 151-162 (1976).
14. Fried, P.A. Short and long-term effects of pre-natal cannabis inhalation upon rat offspring. *Psychopharmacologia* **50** (3); 285-291 (1976).
15. Kennedy, J.S. and Waddell, W.J. Whole body autoradiography of the pregnant mouse after administration of 14-C-delta-9-THC. *Toxicology and Applied Pharmacology* **22**, 252-259 (1972).
16. Dalterio, S. and Bartke, A. Perinatal exposure to cannabinoids alters male reproductive function in mice. *Science* **205**, 1420-1422 (1979).
17. Sassesrath, E.N., et al. Reproduction in Rhesus monkeys chronically exposed to delta-9-THC. In *Marihuana: Biological effects* (Nahas, G.G., and Paton, W.D.M., eds.). Oxford: Pergamon Press (1979), pp. 501-512.
18. Clarren, S. and Smith, D. The fetal alcohol syndrome. *New England Journal of Medicine* **298**: 1063 (1978).

Grass, Genes, and Chromosomes

1. Stenchever, M.A., et al. Chromosome breakage in users of marijuana. *American Journal of Obstetrics and Gynecology* **118**: 106-113 (1974).
2. Kumar, S., and Kunwar, K.B. Chromosome abnormalities on cannabis addicts. *Journal of the Association of Physicians of India* **19**: 193-195 (1972).
3. Martin, P.A., et al. In vivo and invitro studies of the cytogenetic effects of cannabis sativa in rats and men. *Teratology* **9**: 81-86 (1973).
4. Dorrance, D., et al. In vivo effects of illicit hallucinogens on human lymphocyte chromosomes. *Journal of the American Medical Association* **212**: 1488-1491 (1970).
5. Gilmour, D.G., et al. Chromosomal aberrations in users of psychoactive drugs. *Archives of General Psychiatry* **24**: 268-272 (1971).
6. Nichols, W.W., et al. Cytogenetic studies on human subjects receiving marijuana and delta-9-THC. *Mutation Research* **26**: 413-417 (1974).
7. Morishima, A., et al. Effects of marihuana smoking, cannabinoids, and olivetol on replication of human lymphocytes: Formation of micronuclei. In *Pharmacology of Marihuana* (Braude, M.C., and Szara, S., eds.). New York: Raven Press (1976), pp. 711-722.
8. Morishima, A., et al. Hypoploid metophases in cultured lymphocytes of marihuana smokers. In *Marihuana: Biological effects* (Nahas, G.G., and Paton, W.D.M., eds.). Oxford: Pergamon Press (1979) pp. 371-376.

9. Leuchtenberger, C., and Leuchtenberger, R. Correlated cytological and cyto-chemical studies of the effects of fresh smoke from marijuana cigarettes on growth and DNA metabolism of animal and human lung cultures. In *Pharmacology of Marihuana* (Braude, M.C., and Szara, S., eds.). New York: Raven Press (1976), pp. 595-612.
10. Szepsenwol, J., et al. Long term effects of delta-9-THC in mice. In *Marihuana: Biological effects* (Nahas, G.G., and Paton, W.D.M., eds.). Oxford: Pergamon Press (1979) pp. 359-370.
11. Stefanis, C.N., and Issidorides, M.R. Cellular effects of chronic cannabis use in man. In *Marihuana: Chemistry, biochemistry, and cellular effects* (Nahas, G.G., eds.). New York: Springer-Verlag (1976), pp. 533-550.
12. Davidson, W.M., and Smith, D.R. A morphological sex difference in the poly-morphonuclear neutrophyl leukocytes. *British Medical Journal* 2: 6-7 (1954).
13. Zimmerman, A.M., Zimmerman, S., and Raj, A.Y. Effects of cannabinoids on spermatogenesis in mice In *Marihuana: Biological effects* (Nahas, G.G., and Paton, W.D.M., eds.). Oxford: Pergamon Press (1979), pp. 407-418.
14. Hembree, W.C., Zeidenberg, P., and Nahas, G.G. Marihuana's effects on human gonadal function. In *Marihuana: Chemistry, biochemistry, and cellular effects* (Nahas, G.G., eds.). New York: Springer-Verlag (1976), pp. 521-532.

Marijuana and Immunity

1. Gupta, S., et al. Impariment of rosette-forming T-lymphocytes in chronic marihuana smokers. *New England Journal of Medicine* 291: 874-877 (1974).
2. Cushman, P., and Khurana, R. Effects of marihuana smoking and THC on T cell rosettes. *Federation Proceedings* 34: 783 (1975).
3. Silvestein, M.J., and Lessin, P.J. Normal skin test responses in chronic marihuana users. *Science* 186: 740-742 (1974).
4. Nahas, G.G., et al. Inhibition of cell mediated immunity in marijuana smokers. *Science* 183: 419-420 (1974).
5. Moishima, A., et al. Effects of marijuana smoking, cannabinoids, and olivetol on replication of human lymphocytes. In *Pharmacology of Marihuana* (Braude, M.C., and Szara, S., eds.). New York: Raven Press (1976), pp. 711-722.
6. Lau, R.J., et al. Non-inhibition of phytohemagluttinin (PHA) indiced lymphocyte transformation in humans by delta-9-THC. *Federation Proceedings* 34: 783 (1975).
7. White, S.C., et al. Mitogen-induced blastogenic responses of lymphocytes from marihuana smokers. *Science* 188: 71-72 (1975).
8. Daul, C.B., and Heath, R.G. The effect of chronic marihuana usage on the im-munological status of rhesus monkeys. *Life Sciences* 17: 875-882 (1975).
9. Armand, J.P., Hsu, J.T., and Nahas, G.G. Inhibition of blastogenesis of T-lymphocytes by delta-9-THC. *Federation Proceedings* 33: 539 (1974).
10 Rosenkrantz, H. The immune response and marihuana. In *Marihuana: Chemistry, biochemistry, and cellular effects* (Nahas, G.G., eds.). New York: Springer-Verlag (1976), pp. 441-456.
11. Levy, J.A., et al. Effects of delta-9-THC on the immune response of mice. *Federation Proceedings* 34: 782 (1975).
12. Schwartzfarb, L., et al. Dose related inhibition of leukocyte migration by mari-huana and delta-9-THC in vitro. *Journal of Clinical Pharmacology* 14: 35-41 (1974).
13. Gaul, C.C., and Mellors, A. Delta-9-THC and decreased macrophage migration inhibition activity. *Research Communications in Chemical Pathology and Pharmacology* 10: 559-564 (1975).
14. Huber, G.L., et al. An experimental animal model for quantifying the biological effects of marihuana on the defense system of the lung. In *Marihuana: Biological effects* (Nahas, G.G., and Paton, W.D.M., eds.). Oxford: Pergamon Press (1979), pp. 301-328.

Can You Get Hooked?

1. *Marihuana and health: Sixth annual report to the U.S. Congress from the secretary of Health, Education, and Welfare.* Washington, D.C.: U.S. Government Printing Office (1976), pp. 24-25.
2. Tenant, F.S., and Groesbeck, C.J. Psychiatric effects of hashish. *Archives of General Psychiatry* **27**: 133-136 (1972).
3. Carlini, E.A. Tolerance to chronic administration of Cannabis sativa in rats. *Pharmacology* **1**: 135-142 (1968).
4. Gonzalez, S.C., et al. Effects of marihuana compounds on the fighting behavior of Siamese fighting fish (Betta splendens). *Pharmacology* **6**: 168 (1971).
5. McMillan, D.E., et al. 1-delta-9-THC in pigeons: Tolerance to the behavioral effects. *Science* **169**: 501-503 (1970).
6. Abel, E.L. Studies of tolerance to 1-delta-9-THC in neonatal chicks. *Federation Proceedings* **31**: 505 Abs. (1972).
7. Fink, M. Effects of acute and chronic administration of hashish, marijuana, and delta-9-THC on brain electrical activity in man: Evidence for tissue tolerance. *Annals of the New York Academy of Sciences* **282**: 387-398 (1976).
8. Jones, R.T., and Benowitz, N. The 30-day trip — Clinical studies of Cannabis tolerance and dependence. In *Pharmacology of Marihuana* (Braude, M.C., and Szara, S., eds.). New York: Raven Press (1976), pp. 627-642.
9. Mendelson, J.H., et al. Behavioral and biological aspects of marijuana use. *Annals of the New York Academy of Sciences* **282**: 186-210 (1976).
10. Cohen, S. The 94-day cannabis study. *Annals of the New York Academy of Sciences* **282**: 211-220 (1976).
11. Jones, R.T., et al. Clinical studies of Cannabis tolerance and dependence. *Annals of the New York Academy of Sciences* **282**: 221-239.
12. Weil, A.T., Zinberg, N.E., and Nelson, J.M. Clinical and psychological effects of marihuana in man. *Science* **162**: 1234-1242 (1968).
13. Bensusan, A.D. Marihuana withdrawal symptoms. *British Medical Journal* **2**: 112 (1971).
14. Teitel, B. Observations on marihuana withdrawal. *American Journal of Psychiatry* **134**: 587 (1977).
15. Kaymakcalan, S. Physiological and psychological dependence on THC in rhesus monkeys. In *Cannabis and its derivatives* (Paton, W.D.M., and Crown, eds.). Oxford: Oxford University Press (1972), pp. 142-149.
16. Hirschhorn, I.D., and Rosencrans, J.A. Morphine and delta-9-THC: Tolerance to the stimulus effects. *Psychopharmacologia* **36**: 243-253 (1974).
17. Kaymakcalan, S., et al. Naloxone-induced or postwithdrawal abstinence signs in delta-9-treated rats. *Psychopharmacology* **55**: 243 (1977).

In Search of the Perfect Study

1. Rosenkrantz, H., and Fleischman, R.W. Effects of cannabis on lungs. In *Marihuana: Biological effects* (Nahas, G.G., and Paton, W.D.M., eds.). Oxford: Pergamon Press (1979), pp. 279-299.
2. Paton, W.D.M. Concluding summary. In *Marihuana: Biological effects* (Nahas, G.G., and Paton, W.D.M., eds.). Oxford: Pergamon Press (1979), pp. 735-738.
3. Rubin, V., and Comitas, L. *Ganja in Jamaica: A medical anthropological study of chronic marihuana use.* Mouton Press, The Hague (1975).
4. Hall, J.A.S. Testimony before the Senate Subcommittee on Internal Security: "Marihuana-hashish epidemic and its impact on United States security." Hearings of the Committee on the Judiciary, U.S. Senate. Washington, D.C.: U.S. Government Printing Office (1974), pp. 147-154.

A Debate

1. Cancer victims' "pot" use eases nausea of therapy. *Columbus Dispatch,* April 17, 1981, p. A-5 (AP story)
2. Herman, T.S., et al. Superiority of nabilone over prochlorperazine as an antiemetic in patients receiving cancer chemotherapy. *The New England Journal of Medicine* **300:** 1295-1297 (1979).
3. Hart, R.H. Sees no need for THC or marijuana as antiemetic. *Clinical Psychiatry News,* p. 6, Feb., 1981.
4. Newell, F.W., et al. Use of cannabinoid derivatives in glaucoma. *Transactions of the Ophthalmological Society of the United Kingdom* **99:** pp. 269-271 (1979).
5. Gonzalez, E.R. No green light for grass in glaucoma. *Journal of the American medical Association* **244:** 2500 (1980).

What's Normal for NORML?

1. U.S. National Commission on Marihuana and Drug Abuse. *Marihuana: A signal of misunderstanding.* First report: 3 volumes. Washington, D.C.: U.S. Government Printing Office (1972).
2. Brill, H. Testimony before the Senate Subcommittee on Internal Security. *Marihuana-hashish epidemic and its impact on United States security.* Hearings before the Subcommittee to investigate the administration of the Internal Security Act and other internal security laws of the Committee on the Judiciary, United States Senate. Washington, D.C.: U.S. Government Printing Office (1974), pp. 30-36.
3. DuPont, R.L. Press briefing: Some questions and answers. Marihuana and Health: In perspective. *Summary and comments on the Fifth Annual Report to the U.S. Congress from the Secrretary of Health, Education, and Welfare.* Washington, D.C.: U.S. Government Printing Office (1975), pp. 7-12.
4. DuPont, R.L. Foreword. *Marihuana and health: Sixth Annual Report to the U.S. Congress from the Secretary of Health, Education, and Welfare.* Washington, D.C.: U.S. Government Printing Office (1975), p. 49.
5. DuPont, R.L. (interview), "Is U.S. Becoming a Drug-Ridden Society?" *U.S. News & World Report,* Aug. 7, 1978, pp. 30-31.
6. DuPont, R.L., "Marijuana Decriminalization: A Personal Reassessment," A paper presented at the Second Annual Conference on Marijuana, New York, N.Y., June 29, 1979.
7. Stroup, R.K. Testimony before the Senate Subcommittee to Investigate Juvenile Delinquency. *Marihuana decriminalization.* Hearing before the Subcommittee to investigate juvenile delinquency, the Committee on the Judiciary, United States Senate. Washington, D.C.: U.S. Government Printing Office (1975), p. 49.
8. Marijuana festival celebrates 'grass' cult politics, products. *Columbus Dispatch,* Monday, October 29, 1979, p. A-5. (UPI story.)